The Writer's Craft

Spelling and Vocabulary Booklet

Red Level
Grade 7

McDougal Littell Inc.
A Houghton Mifflin Company
Evanston, Illinois   Boston Dallas Phoenix

To the Teacher

The Spelling and Vocabulary Booklet consists of two parts: Spelling Masters and Vocabulary Lessons. A description of each element follows.

Spelling Masters

The ten Spelling Masters for this grade are designed to strengthen students' understanding of key spelling conventions. The lessons can be used for whole-class or small-group instruction or for independent study.

The lesson on each Spelling Master consists of a word list and a spelling generalization followed by three exercises. The word lists are made up of words that students frequently misspell. These words were identified through extensive error analysis of student writing and standardized tests. The first exercise is designed to provide students with practice in writing words from the list. In the second exercise, students are asked to apply the spelling generalization from the lesson to new words. The last exercise makes the connection between spelling and writing by having students proofread writing for errors in grammar, usage, capitalization, and punctuation, in addition to spelling errors related to the generalization presented in the lesson.

Vocabulary Lessons

The vocabulary section is designed to strengthen and expand students' vocabularies and to prepare them to take the Scholastic Assessment Tests. This vocabulary series is based on lists of words frequently found on standardized tests such as the SAT and the ACT. The exercises are similar to the ones students will encounter when they take such tests. There are three booklets, one each for Grades 6–8. Each booklet is composed of 36 vocabulary lessons, and each lesson contains 20 vocabulary words. The parts of speech and definitions of the words are given, along with sample sentences and two sets of exercises.

The words for the vocabulary lessons have been classified by grade level and organized into categories. The use of categories allows students to associate each word with others that are similar in meaning, form, or function. The definitions and the sample sentences correspond to the category in order to provide a context for learning each word. Although many of the words have multiple meanings and forms, the most common definition and part of speech that are appropriate to the category are given for each word.

Each lesson includes a sentence completion exercise followed by a synonym exercise, an antonym exercise, or an analogy exercise. Each word is used at least once in the exercises.

You may wish to introduce the words at the beginning of the week and allow students to complete the exercises as independent study. At the end of the week, you may want to test the students' mastery of the words by asking them to write the words, define them, and use them correctly in original sentences.

ISBN 0-8123-8835-6

4 5 6 7 8 9 10 – MDO – 99 98 97

CONTENTS

Strategies for Teaching Spelling

Research has shown that most students go through several predictable stages of development in learning to spell (Henderson and Beers 1980; Gentry 1984; Henderson 1985; Templeton 1986, 1991; Nelson 1989). These stages may be identified as follows:

1. During the phonetic **letter-name stage,** students conceptualize words in a left-to-right, letter-by-letter fashion. The name of the letter is a primary criterion that students use for spelling a word.
2. In the transitional **written-word-pattern stage,** students begin to use more complex letter sequences in place of the one-letter/one-sound strategy.
3. At the **syllables and affixes stage,** students begin to learn what happens at the juncture where prefixes and suffixes are joined to single-syllable words to form two-syllable words.
4. In the final stage, the **derived forms stage,** students learn more complex word information based on meanings, such as related word forms, root words, and words derived from other languages.

Students in grades 6–8 most commonly function within the third and fourth stages of spelling development. For example, students at stage three are likely to make spelling errors in words that require doubling a final consonant or dropping a final *e* before adding a suffix that begins with a vowel: droping *(dropping),* makeing *(making).* At stage four, students' errors tend to reflect their continuing attention to sound rather than the meaning characteristics of words: *musision (musician).* The Spelling Masters address the most common kinds of errors made by students at these stages. They can be adapted to a prescriptive approach or presented as traditional spelling lessons.

Prescriptive Approach

Using this approach, the teacher regularly analyzes the errors in a student's writing, making notes about the type and frequency of errors. Writing samples from all subject areas should be examined. When a pattern of errors emerges, that is, when a student consistently misspells words containing a particular letter pattern, the teacher points out the problem to the student and presents the lesson that addresses that spelling generalization. If the teacher discovers that several students or the entire class are making the same type of error, any lesson may also be used for small-group or whole-class instruction. Note that, using a prescriptive approach, the lessons may be presented out of order, and some lessons may not be used at all.

Traditional Approach

Using a traditional approach, the Spelling Masters would be presented to the class in the order they appear in this book. To teach the lesson, the teacher might present the word list and spelling generalization on Monday and have the class work through the exercises independently. Later in the week, the exercises would be corrected orally.

No matter which approach you choose you might suggest that students use one or more of the following strategies to improve their spelling:

1. Encourage students to keep a personal spelling journal in which they list in alphabetical order the troublesome words or words they wish to learn. Suggest that students highlight or underline elements of the word that they find especially tricky or difficult to remember.
2. When students are learning to spell new words, encourage them to use an approach that engages a variety of senses. Such an approach might involve visual study of the word, oral practice, mental imaging, and written practice. For example these procedures could be followed:

    Look at the word.
    Say the word.
    Spell the word.
    Copy the word.
    Picture the word.
    Cover the word and write it.
3. Suggest that students create mnemonic devices and other memory aids to help them remember the lesson pattern. One such aid might be the phrase "the amazing disappearing *e*."

References

Gentry, J. Richard. "Developmental Aspects of Learning to Spell." *Academic Therapy* 20 (Sept. 1984): 11-19.

Henderson, Edmund H. *Teaching Spelling.* Boston: Houghton Mifflin, 1985.

Henderson, Edmund H., and James W. Beers, eds. *Developmental and Cognitive Aspects of Learning to Spell: A Reflection of Word Knowledge.* Newark, Del.: International Reading Association, 1980.

Nelson, Laurie. "Something Borrowed, Something New: Teaching Implications of Developmental Spelling Research." *Reading Psychology* 10.2-3 (1989)

Templeton, Shane. "Synthesis of Research on the Learning and Teaching of Spelling." *Educational Leadership* 43 (Mar. 1986): 73-78.

———. "Teaching and Learning the English Spelling System: Reconceptualizing Method and Purpose." *The Elementary School Journal* 92.2 (Nov. 1991)

Spelling Master 1
Final silent e words and suffixes

sincere	sincerity	sincerely
separate	separating	separately
name	naming	namely
hope	hoping	hopeful
waste	wasting	wasteful
forgive	forgivable	forgiveness
require	requiring	requirement
place	placing	placement
involve	involving	involvement
improve	improving	improvement

A **suffix** is a word ending that changes the use of a word.

When you add a suffix that begins with a vowel to a word that ends with a silent *e*, drop the final *e*. Keep the *e* if the suffix begins with a consonant.

Exceptions: true—truly   argue—argument   awe—awful
whole—wholly   nine—ninth

Practice the Words
Complete each sentence with a related form of the word in parentheses. On the line at the right, write the word you choose.

1. The coach is (place) _____ your trophy in
the display case.   _____

2. People can stop (waste) _____ water by turning
off the faucet when they brush their teeth.   _____

3. One (require) _____ our school has adopted
is that all students follow a dress code.   _____

4. If our new baby is a boy, we are (name) _____
him Alberto after my grandfather.   _____

5. By (improve) _____ their skills, athletes can win
more games and set new records.   _____

6. People who show (sincere) _____ are respected.   _____

7. It is difficult for some people to ask for (forgive) _____.   _____

8. I am (hope) _____ that a cure for cancer will
be found in my lifetime.   _____

9. Our teacher believes that (separate) _____ boys
   and girls into different teams is unfair.
   _____

10. By (involve) _____ more students in the school play,
    we hope to get a bigger audience.
    _____

Apply What You Know

Add the suffixes indicated, and write the new word on the line.

1. mature + -ity =   _____

2. creative + -ly =   _____

3. believe + -able =   _____

4. revise + -ion =   _____

5. continue + -ous =   _____

6. scarce + -ly =   _____

7. amaze + -ment =   _____

8. culture + -al =   _____

9. care + -ful =   _____

10. insure + -ance =   _____

Proofreading Practice

Proofread the following article for a school newspaper. Mark the mistakes in grammar,
capitalization, punctuation, and spelling.

DODGEING DUMB DARES

Are you troubled by friends dareing you to do mean or dangerous things

like teasing kids or stealing valueables! What would you do if these kinds

of dares were a requirment for getting into a special club or cool crowd.

here are some useable strategies for ignoring a dare without loseing a

friend or causing an arguement. Try making up an excuse changeing the

subject, or walking away. Better yet, stand up for what is write or point out

the stupidity of engaging in dangerous activities.

Spelling Master 2

Final y words and suffixes

spray	sprays	sprayed	spraying
display	displays	displayed	displaying
enjoy	enjoys	enjoyed	enjoying
holiday	holidays		
journey	journeys		
reply	replies	replied	replying
steady	steadies	steadied	steadying
empty	empties	emptied	emptying
balcony	balconies		
county	counties		

> If the letter before a final **y** is a vowel, do not change the **y** when you add a suffix.
>
> Exception: day + -*ly* = daily
>
> If the letter before a final **y** is a consonant, change the **y** to **i** before you add any suffix except **-ing**. The **y** never changes before **-ing**.
>
> Exceptions: dry + -*ness* = dryness   shy + -*ness* = shyness

Practice the Words

Complete these analogies. Determine the relationship between the original pair of words. Then write the spelling word that has this same relationship with the third word. Be sure to use the appropriate **-s, -ed,** or **-ing** form.

1. **Yards** are to **inches** as **states** are to _____.

2. **Rising** is to **falling** as **filling** is to _____.

3. **Explorations** are to **searches** as **treks** are to _____.

4. **Drizzled** is to **poured** as **sprinkled** is to _____.

5. **Asked** is to **questioned** as **answered** is to _____.

6. **Loving** is to **hating** as **disliking** is to _____.

7. **Fences** are to **yards** as **railings** are to _____.

8. **Hiding** is to **concealing** as **exhibiting** is to _____.

9. **Work** is to **weekdays** as **celebration** is to _____.

10. **Bending** is to **straightening** as **shaking** is to _____.

Apply What You Know

To complete the chart, fill in the empty boxes by writing the base word and the *-s, -ed,* and *-ing* forms of the words in each row.

Base Word	-s	-ed	-ing
1. survey			
2.			envying
3. stay			
4. multiply			
5.		satisfied	
6. pity			
7.	relays		
8. annoy			
9. notify			
10.			carrying

Proofreading Practice

Proofread the course description that follows. Mark the mistakes in grammar, capitalization, punctuation, and spelling.

Do you want to earn more money as a baby sitter and have your choice

of the most envyable jobs in the neighborhood? If so, learn to improve

your skills by taking the baby-sitting course at Mercy hospital. The

saturday morning classes are held in laboratoryes and taught by certifed

instructors. You will learn about child safety and baby-sitting procedures,

including lessons on how babys should be carryed, when parents should

be notified, what to do when emergences arise, and how to entertain kids.

The course are open to boys and girls ages twelve to sixteen.

Spelling Master 3
Adding suffixes

plan	planning	planned	
star	starring	starred	
slip	slipped	slippery	
sad	sadder	saddest	sadness
dim	dimmed	dimmer	dimly
seat	seating	seated	
wait	waiting	waited	
sleep	sleeping	sleepy	
darn	darning	darned	
chair	chairing	chaired	

> A word that has **1** syllable, **1** vowel, and **1** final consonant is called a
> **1 + 1 + 1** word. To add a suffix beginning with a vowel to a **1 + 1 + 1** word,
> first double the final consonant: plan—planned. Do not double the final
> consonant when adding a suffix that begins with a consonant.
>   For one-syllable words that are not **1 + 1 + 1** words, do not double the
> final consonant.

Practice the Words
To each base word add the suffixes indicated. Write the new word on the line.

1. sad + -est = _____

2. dim + -ly = _____

3. seat + -ed = _____

4. chair + -ing = _____

5. star + -ed = _____

6. darn + -ing = _____

7. plan + -ed = _____

8. wait + -ing = _____

9. slip + -ery = _____

10. sleep + -y = _____

Now complete each of the sentences with one of the words you wrote.

a. The usher _____ the patron.

b. By _____ his socks, Chris made them last longer.

c. Carlos _____ in the role of Scrooge.

d. We were _____ in line for hours.

e. Ana had the _____ expression on her face!

f. The _____ pavement caused the car to skid.

g. The baby slept best in a _____ lit room.

h. "The Legend of _____ Hollow" is an exciting story.

i. Kim is _____ the Art Club meeting.

j. Felix _____ the class picnic.

Apply What You Know

Complete the crossword puzzle. Use the base words below and the suffixes *-ed, -ing,
-en, -er,* and *-est* to form words suggested by the numbered clues. Remember that
adding a suffix can sometimes change the meaning of a base word. Use a dictionary if
you need help.

rob	stop	shoot	fat	turn	big	swim	stir
bag	grab	skirt	meet	pin	jog	ship	

Across

2. Grasped
6. Mixing
8. Rotating
9. To make plump
10. Halted
12. Moving along the edge
13. A kind of runner
14. Luggage

Down

1. Gathering
3. A burglar
4. Opposite of littlest
5. Sent or transported
7. Firing
10. An aquatic athlete
11. Fastened

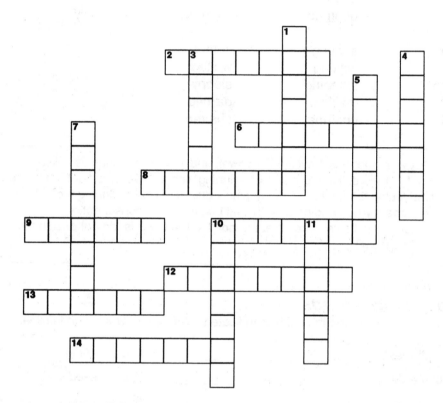

Proofreading Practice

Proofread this excerpt from a research report on animal survival skills. Mark the
mistakes in grammar, capitalization, punctuation, and spelling.

While spiting may be impolite for humans, it is actually a survival skill for many animals.

One kind of cobra, for instance, can spit its venom into the face of an enemy standing eight

feet away! Adult archerfish can spit even farther. Swiming just under the surface, these fish

are experts at spoting bugs on plants, shootting a stream of water at the bugs, and then

catching the bugs in their mouths In turn, "walking worms" catch insects by squirtting a

slime over them The slime hardens into a cage. Camels and Llamas will spit right in the

face of anyone who upset them so watch out for these animals or you may get zaped!

Spelling Master 4
More about adding suffixes

begin	beginning	beginner	
rebel	rebelled	rebellion	
equip	equipping	equipped	equipment
commit	committing	committee	commitment
confer	conferring	conferred	conference
refer	referring	referred	reference
differ	differing	differed	difference
suffer	suffering	suffered	
offer	offering	offered	
visit	visiting	visitor	

Before adding a suffix beginning with a vowel to a word of two or more syllables, double the final consonant only if both of the following conditions exist:

1. The word ends with a single consonant preceded by a single vowel.
2. The word is accented on the last syllable: up set'.

Note: If the newly formed word is accented on a different syllable, the final consonant is not doubled: con fer' con' fer ence.

Practice the Words
Write the spelling word that is related in some way to each group of words.

1. guest, caller, company _____

2. tools, implements, material _____

3. gift, donation, present _____

4. amateur, novice, apprentice _____

5. dictionary, encyclopedia, thesaurus _____

6. pain, misery, difficulty _____

7. conversing, discussing, talking _____

8. uprising, resistance, revolution _____

9. council, board, panel _____

10. contrasting, disagreeing, opposing _____

Apply What You Know

Mark the accented syllable in each base word below. Then, on the spaces provided, use the clue to write a related form of the word. If a newly formed word is accented on a different syllable, circle the word. Use a dictionary if you need help.

con trol	pi lot	re fer	pro pel
for get	pre fer	hap pen	trans mit

1. a revolving blade on an airplane or boat (n.): __ __ __ __ __ __ __ __ __ __

2. something sent out or passed along (n.): __ __ __ __ __ __ __ __ __ __ __ __

3. the directing of someone to a person or place (n.): __ __ __ __ __ __ __ __ __ __

4. one's first choice (n.): __ __ __ __ __ __ __ __ __ __ __

5. guiding or leading (v.): __ __ __ __ __ __ __ __ __

6. not memorable (adj.): __ __ __ __ __ __ __ __ __ __ __ __

7. an incident or event (n.): __ __ __ __ __ __ __ __ __ __

8. a person or device that guides (n.): __ __ __ __ __ __ __ __ __ __ __ __

Proofreading Practice

Proofread the science copy that follows. Mark the mistakes in grammar, capitalization, punctuation, and spelling.

In 1989 the space Shuttle *Atlantis* propeled the *Magellan* toward Venus.

The *Magellan* differed from other spacecraft that had orbitted Venus,

before 1989, because it transmited radar images of Venus's surface more

clear than the others did. These images showed that Venus is coverred

with volcanoes. Scientists think that magma expeled from the volcanoes is

responsible for the spidery formations seen on Venus and not seen on

other planets.

Spelling Master 5
Adding prefixes

re-	+ commend	=	recommend	*in-*	+ vent + *-ion*	=	invention
ex-	+ claim	=	exclaim	*pre-*	+ vent + *-ion*	=	prevention
sub-	+ urban	=	suburban	*in-*	+ clude	=	include
pro-	+ pose	=	propose	*ex-*	+ clude	=	exclude
con-	+ sequence	=	consequence	*con-*	+ clude	=	conclude

A **base word** is a complete word to which other word parts can be added.
A **root** is a word part that cannot stand alone. It becomes a word when it is joined with a prefix or a suffix.

Prefix		Root		Word
	+		=	
in-		clude		include

A **prefix** is a group of letters added to the beginning of a word or root to change its meaning. When a prefix is added to a word, the spelling of the base word or root remains the same.

Practice the Words
Complete each sentence below by filling in the blank with one or more words from the list.

1. In 1834, Henry Blair became one of the first African Americans to receive a patent

   for a(n) _____.

2. In the famous Greek myth of Daedalus and Icarus, Icarus's wax wings melt and he

   falls to his death as a _____ of flying too close to the sun.

3. The chief of the local fire department spoke to our class about fire _____.

4. People who live in _____ areas sometimes travel to a
   larger city to work and for cultural activities.

5. On February 18, 1930, no one else was around to hear astronomer Clyde Tombaugh

   _____ "That's it!" when he discovered the planet Pluto.

6. Based on the tracks we found in the dirt, we were able to _____
   that the bear was injured.

7. Mei-Leng would like to attend the party and asked if you would please

   _____ her on your list.

8. The president plans to _____ a tax increase when he
   addresses Congress.

9. Nutritionists generally _____ a daily diet that includes more than one serving from each of the five basic food groups.

10. The Immigration and Naturalization Service has the authority to admit,

_____, and deport aliens according to the immigration laws.

Apply What You Know

Choose one of the prefixes to add to each base word or root below, and write the new word on the line. In some cases more than one word may be formed. Circle whether the word is composed of a base word or root.

Prefixes:	de-	pre-	re-	in-	pro-	con-

1. _____ + serve = _____   base word   root

2. _____ + sist = _____   base word   root

3. _____ + tect = _____   base word   root

4. _____ + form = _____   base word   root

5. _____ + code = _____   base word   root

6. _____ + quest = _____   base word   root

7. _____ + ject = _____   base word   root

8. _____ + dict = _____   base word   root

9. _____ + part = _____   base word   root

10. _____ + long = _____   base word   root

Proofreading Practice

Proofread this first draft of a science article. Mark the mistakes in grammar, capitalization, punctuation, and spelling.

To iksplore the deep ocean, scientists needed an envention that could proform

under harsh conditions and for prelonged periods of time. It would have to pervide

air, light, pressurization, and communication. The result was a small submarine

name *alvin. Alvin,* holds three passengers and submmerges to depths of 7,500

feet. It allows scientists to explore a previously encharted frontier.

Spelling Master 6
Unstressed syllables

relative	related	fantasy	fantastic
human	humanity	democracy	democratic
grammar	grammatical	comedy	comedian
remedy	remedial	hostile	hostility
editor	editorial	confide	confidence

> Unstressed vowels cause spelling problems because they are difficult to hear and identify. A vowel in an accented syllable is pronounced more clearly: com′ e dy   co me′ di an.
>
> Many words have a form in which the accent shifts to a different syllable. If you are unsure of how to spell a word that has an unstressed vowel, think of a related form of the word. The pronunciation of that word will help you identify the correct vowel.

Practice the Words

Answer each question with a sentence that contains a spelling word. The underlined word or phrase will guide you in choosing the best word.

1. What did you think of the <u>opinion column</u> in the newspaper? _____

_____

2. Is the man in the blue shirt a <u>member of your family</u>? _____

_____

3. What kind of error would result if you said <u>"between you and I" instead of "between you and me"</u>?

_____

4. What responsibility do citizens have in a <u>government that is run by the people</u>?

_____

5. How can a person gain more <u>self-assurance</u>? _____

_____

6. Which type of monkey do you think looks and acts the most <u>like people</u>? _____

_____

7. Is there any way I can <u>get over</u> this cold? _____

_____

8. Do you want to watch a serious show or <u>a show that will make you laugh</u>?_____

_____

9. Why is Gwen showing so much <u>unfriendliness</u> toward Kate?_____

_____

10. Do you think people will live on the moon someday, or is that just a <u>daydream</u>?

_____

Apply What You Know

Add the missing letter and mark the accented syllable in each word below. Then follow the instructions to change each word to a related form. Write the new word in syllables and mark the accent. Use your dictionary if you need help.

1. bi ol __ gy   Drop the **y**, add **-Ical**.   _____

2. an g__l   Add **-Ic**.   _____

3. phi los __ phy   Drop the **y**, add **-Ic**.   _____

4. in f__ nite   Drop the **e**, add **-y**.   _____

5. mol __ cule   Drop the final **e**, add **-ar**.   _____

6. spon ta n__ ous   Drop the **-ous**, add **-Ity**.   _____

7. ge og r__ phy   Drop the **y**, add **-Ical**.   _____

8. im pr__ vise   Drop the **e**, add **-atIon**.   _____

Proofreading Practice

Proofread this excerpt from a letter. Mark the mistakes in grammar, capitalization, punctuation, and spelling.

Last week I went to an improvasational comedy club called The Funny Place. It

is a place where young comiedians perform humorous skits. One skit was about a

student studying human anatamy in a biolegy class. The jokes and the

expressions was hilarious! Speaking of classes, I am really starting to like my

geogrophy class. Ever since I went to visit my relitives in Mexico, I have taken a

greater interest in learning about foreign countries. I just remembered I have a

grammer quiz tomorrow, so I better start studying. I hope to hear from you soon.

Spelling Master 7
Silent gh

<u>ough</u>t	sl<u>igh</u>t
alth<u>ough</u>	s<u>igh</u>tseeing
thr<u>ough</u>out	he<u>igh</u>t
thor<u>ough</u>ly	we<u>igh</u>ed
d<u>augh</u>ter	<u>eigh</u>tieth

The letters *gh* are often silent in a few familiar letter combinations:

    ou*gh*   **au*gh***   **i*ght***   **ei*gh***

Practice the Words

Circle the word in each phrase that is similar in meaning to a spelling word. Write the spelling word on the line beside the phrase. Expand each phrase into a sentence in which the word you circled is replaced with the spelling word.

1. a small scratch   _____

_____

2. a week of touring in Rome   _____

_____

3. completely soaked   _____

_____

4. an octogenarian birthday   _____

_____

5. though we were tired   _____

_____

6. only one girl   _____

_____

7. all over the United States   _____

_____

Name ____ Date ______________

8. should be allowed ____________________

____

9. measured the amount ____________________

____

10. elevation of the mountain ____________________

____

Apply What You Know

The scrambled words below contain the letter combinations ***igh*** or ***eigh.*** Unscramble the words by solving the puzzles. Write the new words in the boxes.

tyimgh   gibonhrodohe   tgpriyohc   hrgitefnde   ehfldtiulg

1. my + 

m					y

2.  + bor + 

n											d

3.  +  + 

c			y					t

4.  + 10 + ed

f							n		

5. D +  + ful

		l							

Proofreading Practice

Proofread the police bulletins that follow. Mark the mistakes in grammar, capitalization, punctuation, and spelling.

WANTED: Tommy the Terrible, a thoroghly thaughtless thief wieghing 180 pounds, is wanted for robbery. Tommy faught his way out of the County Jail. And may be living in you're nieghborhood. A reward is offerred for information leading to his arrest.

STOLEN: The Eigth Wonder of the World Tour Company have reported that there siteseeing bus has been stole. A search thruout the county should be made. Contact Ms. Page, the owner's doughter for more details.

Spelling Master 8
Words ending in -able/-ible

avail   + -able = available
agree   + -able = agreeable
regret + -able = regrettable

advise + -able = advisable
notice + -able = noticeable
manage + -able = manageable

vis + -ible = visible
leg + -ible = legible
aud + -ible = audible
ed + -ible = edible

The suffix **-able** is commonly added to complete words to form adjectives meaning "able to be." When **-able** is added to words that end in **ce** or **ge,** the **e** must be kept to retain the soft sound of **c** or **g.**

The suffix **-ible** is more commonly added to roots than to complete words. The **I** in **-ible** gives the letter **g** a soft sound: le*g*ible tan*g*ible.

Mnemonic device: Many words that begin with **a** use the suffix that begins with **a.**

Practice the Words
Write the spelling word that is suggested by each situation.

1. _____ After the fog lifted, the mountain peak came into sight.

2. _____ The package is small enough for me to handle.

3. _____ Ana did not know that she could eat the clear wrapper on the rice candy.

4. _____ The improvement in Lewis's pitching is apparent and has drawn the attention of Major League scouts.

5. _____ It is a shame that more people do not try to reduce, reuse, and recycle for the sake of the environment.

6. _____ The child was polite and had a pleasant disposition.

7. _____ The manager said that the video will be released in March and that she will have a copy of it on the shelf.

8. _____ Our teacher taught us how to project our voices so that people sitting in the back row could hear us.

9. _____ It is wise to rest if you are feeling sick.

10. _____ Her handwriting is both beautiful and easy to read.

Apply What You Know

Circle the first letter of each word in the nonsense sentences below to find a base word or root. Write it on the line. Then add the suffix and write the new word.

1. All dragons are predictably temperamental.

_____ + -able = _____

2. Careful orangutans never try rousing ornery lions.

_____ + l + -able = _____

3. Cultured rhinoceroses eat daintily.

_____ + -ible = _____

4. Conceited horses are not gracious entertainers.

_____ + -able = _____

5. Tapirs are notoriously gullible.

_____ + -ible = _____

Proofreading Practice

Proofread this paragraph from a brochure on recycling. Mark the mistakes in grammar, capitalization, punctuation, and spelling.

Many companies claim that their packages are not harmful to the

environment, but how do you know if those claims are credable? First,

remember that a truly biodegradeable product is one that is perishible, like

a banana peel. Air sunlight, and moisture must be available to break

substances down. Thus, products like Disposeable diapers that are

dumped in landfills and covered with garbage can't decompose. Second

many items that are said to be recycleable are rarely recycled. So check

whether a product is acceptible in your area before you buy it. It's not

recyclable if there are no place for you to recycle it.

Words ending in -ous/us and -ize/ise

adventure + *-ous* = adventur<u>ous</u>   apology + *-ize* = apolog<u>ize</u>
courage + *-ous* = courage<u>ous</u>   critic   + *-ize* = critic<u>ize</u>
outrage + *-ous* = outrage<u>ous</u>   sympathy + *-ize* = sympath<u>ize</u>

geni<u>us</u>   telev<u>ise</u>
surpl<u>us</u>   advert<u>ise</u>
vir<u>us</u>   desp<u>ise</u>

The suffix *-ous* is added to words to form adjectives meaning "full of" or "having certain characteristics."
The *us* spelling is not a suffix. It is a noun ending.
The suffix *-ize* is added to words to form verbs meaning "to make or become."
The *ise* spelling is an ending, not a suffix.

Practice the Words
Write the spelling word that is related in some way to each group of words.

1. talent, intelligence, brilliance   _____

2. hate, loathe, scorn   _____

3. daring, reckless, adventuresome   _____

4. announce, declare, publicize   _____

5. analyze, judge, blame   _____

6. brave, fearless, valiant   _____

7. leftover, remainder, excess   _____

8. shameless, shocking, bizarre   _____

9. disease, sickness, illness   _____

10. understand, support, comfort   _____

11. transmit, broadcast, telecast   _____

12. confess, admit, ask forgiveness   _____

Apply What You Know

Analyze the words below. Then write each word in the appropriate column on the chart.

bonus	continuous	concise	customize	mischievous
exercise	compromise	census	momentous	memorize

Has a Suffix   **Does Not Have a Suffix**

_____   _____

_____   _____

_____   _____

_____   _____

_____   _____

Proofreading Practice

Proofread the following advertisements. Mark the mistakes in grammar, capitalization, punctuation, and spelling.

Circus Extravaganza!

March 22–31

PBS, Channel 11

Circus Extravaganza, a nationally

televised circus, features coragous

lion tamers gorgous horses,

mischivous monkeys, and a

charmer of poisonus snakes!

Don't miss it!

Customised stationery

Consultants

We specialized in personalised

envelopes and writing paper for the

home and office. Call one of are

sales representatives for a free

brochure!

555–3624

Spelling Master 10
Words ending in -ance/-ant and -ence/-ent

attend + *-ance* = attend<u>ance</u>	defend + *-ant* = defend<u>ant</u>
annoy + *-ance* = annoy<u>ance</u>	inhabit + *-ant* = inhabit<u>ant</u>
defy + *-ance* = defi<u>ance</u>	descend + *-ant* = descend<u>ant</u>

consci<u>ence</u>   anci<u>ent</u>
sequ<u>ence</u>   effici<u>ent</u>
sci<u>ence</u>   frequ<u>ent</u>

> The suffixes **-ance** and **-ant** are commonly added to complete words.
> The suffixes **-ence** and **-ent** are commonly used with roots. They are used after the letters *cl, qu,* and *sc.*
>
> Mnemonic: Many words that begin with the letter *a* use the suffix that begins with the letter *a.*

Practice the Words
Complete these analogies. Determine the relationship between the original pair of words. Then write the spelling word that has this same relationship with the third word.

1. **Grandfather** is to **ancestor** as **child** is to _____.

2. **Doubt** is to **certainty** as **absence** is to _____.

3. **Algebra** is to **math** as **biology** is to _____.

4. **Contemporary** is to **old** as **modern** is to _____.

5. **Doctor** is to **patient** as **lawyer** is to _____.

6. **Joy** is to **delight** as **irritation** is to _____.

7. **Cave** is to **dweller** as **country** is to _____.

8. **Useful** is to **practical** as **timesaving** is to _____.

9. **Seldom** is to **usual** as **rare** is to _____.

10. **Disorder** is to **chaos** as **order** is to _____.

11. **Willingness** is to **obedience** as **rebellion** is to _____.

12. **Knowledge** is to **intelligence** as **morality** is to _____.

Apply What You Know

Use the pronunciations, the part of speech labels, and the definitions given below to write eight new words that fit the spelling pattern taught in this lesson.

1. _____ (ə void' 'ns) *n.* the act of keeping away from something

2. _____ (sə fish' ənt) *adj.* as much as needed; enough

3. _____ (kres' ənt) *n.* the moon in its first or last quarter

4. _____ (ə plī'əns) *n.* 1. the act of applying 2. a mechanical or electrical device or machine for performing tasks

5. _____ (kən test' ənt) *n.* a person who competes in a contest

6. _____ (di liŋ' kwənt) *adj.* failing to do what duty or law requires

7. _____ (ad' 'l es 'ns) *n.* the time of life between puberty and maturity

8. _____ (trī um' fənt) *adj.* successful; victorious

Proofreading Practice

Proofread these plot summaries of possible television shows. Mark the mistakes in grammar, capitalization, punctuation, and spelling.

PLANET OF THE GRAPES   The Bacchians, anceint inhabitents of

the planet bacchus act in defience of

the law by imprisoning the cresent-

shaped creatures known as The Grape

Eaters

AS THE WORLD ERUPTS   A new science program on how we can

safely and efficiantly harnessed the

energy from volcanic eruptions to

power our electrical appliences.

Lesson 1
Cuisine

All the words in this lesson may be associated with cooking.

basic ADJ. fundamental, essential (Learning how to measure ingredients accurately is a *basic* cooking skill.)

broil V. to cook over or beneath an open flame (In summer we *broil* hamburgers on the barbecue grill.)

broth N. a thin, clear soup (Adding vegetables to the chicken *broth* will add flavor.)

congeal V. to become solid as cooling occurs (The fat from the cooked hamburgers will *congeal* when the pan gets cold.)

crystallize V. to become solid in the form of crystals (The sugar in honey will often *crystallize* on the sides of the jar.)

culinary ADJ. having to do with cooking (On the cooking show, many *culinary* topics were discussed.)

dehydrated ADJ. preserved by removing water (*Dehydrated* foods are good to take on camping trips because they are lightweight and easy to prepare.)

digestion N. the changing of food into a form that the body can take in and use (If you exercise too soon after a meal, your *digestion* may be affected.)

extract N. a concentrated flavoring (The baker always added vanilla *extract* to his sugar cookies.)

ferment V. a change in food from one form to another caused by yeast or bacteria (As fruit *ferments,* sugar is changed to alcohol.)

immerse V. to plunge into or cover with liquid (To make peeling easier, *immerse* peaches briefly in boiling water.)

implement N. a utensil or useful device (A simple but helpful kitchen *implement* is a wooden spoon.)

meringue N. egg whites stiffly beaten and mixed with sugar (A lemon pie is often served with a fluffy *meringue* topping.)

omelet N. beaten eggs cooked until firm and folded over (Cheese and ham were added to the *omelet* before it was taken out of the pan.)

pungent ADJ. having a penetrating taste or smell (The *pungent* odor of garlic filled our kitchen.)

rind N. The firm outer covering of certain foods (Peter peeled off the thick *rind* of the orange and ate a juicy section.)

savor V. to enjoy fully and unhurriedly (Sam ate slowly in order to *savor* each bite of the roasted duck.)

subtle ADJ. not obvious or immediately noticeable (The *subtle* taste of cinnamon indicated that only a small amount of the spice had been used.)

sumptuous ADJ. lavish, splendid (At the royal banquet, a *sumptuous* meal was enjoyed by all the guests.)

vegetarian ADJ. without meat, poultry, or fish (Because she did not approve of killing animals, Marta ate only *vegetarian* dishes.)

Exercise 1
Write the letter of the word that best completes the sentence.

1. The melted chocolate will _____ unless you spread it quickly. _____
   A. ferment   B. broil   C. congeal   D. savor

2. The white mounds of _____ covered the pie. _____
   A. rind   B. meringue   C. broth   D. omelet

3. As soy beans _____, the liquid that is formed is used in soy sauce. _____

    A. ferment   B. broil   C. congeal   D. immerse

4. During the process of _____, food is turned into energy for your body. _____

    A. omelet   B. extract   C. implement   D. digestion

5. The salt in water will _____ when the water evaporates. _____

    A. immerse   B. crystallize   C. ferment   D. broil

6. Tyrone used a package of _____ onion instead of cutting up a fresh one. _____

    A. subtle   B. basic   C. vegetarian   D. dehydrated

7. If you like eggs, you can have a(n) _____ for dinner. _____

    A. broth   B. implement   C. omelet   D. meringue

8. Good cooks are usually proud of their _____ skills. _____

    A. culinary   B. vegetarian   C. sumptuous   D. subtle

9. The hot beef _____ was tasty but not very filling. _____

    A. meringue   B. broth   C. rind   D. omelet

10. Because it was a _____ lasagna, it did not contain meat. _____

    A. subtle   B. pungent   C. culinary   D. vegetarian

Exercise 2

Write the letter of the word that most nearly has the *same* meaning as the italicized word.

11. *basic*	A. heavy	B. elementary	C. thoughtful	D. difficult	_____
12. *pungent*	A. strong	B. simple	C. oiled	D. sad	_____
13. *rind*	A. see	B. root	C. frost	D. skin	_____
14. *savor*	A. rescue	B. describe	C. appreciate	D. cut	_____
15. *implement*	A. water	B. tool	C. spice	D. wax	_____
16. *sumptuous*	A. silly	B. fried	C. extravagant	D. slippery	_____
17. *broil*	A. simmer	B. freeze	C. grill	D. whip	_____
18. *extract*	A. candy	B. concentrate	C. calorie	D. mixture	_____
19. *subtle*	A. faint	B. strong	C. huge	D. hard	_____
20. *immerse*	A. divide	B. drown	C. roll	D. dry	_____

Lesson 2
Sports

All the words in this lesson may be associated with sports.

ability   N. talent; skill (John played quarterback because of his *ability* to throw the long pass.)

accurate   ADJ. exact, correct (An archer's aim must be *accurate* to hit the bull's eye on the target.)

agile   ADJ. able to move quickly and easily (The skater's *agile* movements made the crowd cheer loudly.)

ascend   V. go up; climb (She wanted to be the first woman to *ascend* Mt. Everest.)

compete   V. to try to win something wanted by others (Thirty-two teams were scheduled to *compete* for the state soccer championship.)

croquet   N. an outdoor game in which players knock wooden balls through small wire hoops with long handled mallets (People who like to play *croquet* say it is a perfect way to spend a summer afternoon.)

defeat   V. to win over (Everybody in school was hoping our volleyball team would *defeat* last year's champion.)

defend   V. to protect (In hockey, the goalie's main job is to *defend* the goal to keep the other team from scoring.)

encourage   V. to give hope; cheer (A good coach must try to *encourage* players even when they are losing.)

extremely   ADV. very (The back flip is an *extremely* difficult dive to master.)

flexible   ADJ. easily bent; not stiff (To be a good wrestler, you need a *flexible* body.)

freestyle   ADJ. free choice of style or method (*Freestyle* skiing is exciting to watch because the skiers are always flying through the air.)

league   N. a group of people or players working together (After playing softball every Saturday for a month, the teachers finally decided to start a softball *league*.)

leisure   ADJ. free time from work (Participating in sports activities is a good way to spend your *leisure* time.)

offense   N. the person or team attacking (When our *offense* has the ball, you can be sure we will score lots of points.)

perform   V. to present publicly (An athlete must be ready to *perform* on the day of the game.)

serious   ADJ. earnest, requiring effort (The *serious* downhill ski racer trains for many hours to prepare for the World Championships.)

svelte   ADJ. slender (The *svelte* tennis player's thin arms looked weak, but they were powerful.)

uniform   N. an outfit worn by members of a group (I like my baseball *uniform*.)

victory   N. the winning over one's opponent (Our first *victory* of the season occurred when we beat Elm Jr. High School by ten points.)

Exercise 1
Write the letter of the word that best completes the sentence.

1. In the _____ competition, skaters can choose to skate in any style they like.   _____
   A. svelte   B. serious   C. freestyle   D. accurate

2. The team's _____ is so weak that they never score a single goal.   _____
   A. uniform   B. croquet   C. victory   D. offense

3. The _____ dancer had a narrow waist.   _____
   A. svelte   B. serious   C. accurate   D. freestyle

4. The gymnast had to _____ without making a mistake to win the gold medal.
   A. ascend   B. perform   C. defeat   D. encourage   _____

5. Athletic _____ is important, but practice can make an average player into a star.
   A. ability   B. victory   C. uniform   D. croquet   _____

6. I dislike _____ because I can never hit the ball with the mallet.
   A. offense   B. ability   C. uniform   D. croquet   _____

7. With just seconds remaining in the game, we were not sure if _____ would be ours.
   A. ability   B. victory   C. offense   D. uniform   _____

8. We formed a soccer _____ so we could attract new players.
   A. victory   B. uniform   C. offense   D. league   _____

9. The forward on our team has the most _____ jump shot I've ever seen.
   A. svelte   B. accurate   C. leisure   D. freestyle   _____

10. By giving workshops, the tennis pros will _____ young players to play the game.
   A. encourage   B. ascend   C. perform   D. compete   _____

11. The _____ shortstop moved quickly from one part of the field to the other.
   A. svelte   B. agile   C. leisure   D. freestyle   _____

12. During her _____ hours after work, Anita dresses comfortably in sweatpants and an old T-shirt.
   A. serious   B. svelte   C. leisure   D. agile   _____

13. Cliff divers must first _____ two-hundred-foot cliffs so they can dive into the water below.
   A. defeat   B. perform   C. defend   D. ascend   _____

14. Driving at speeds up to 200 miles per hour is not unusual for the _____ race car driver.
   A. flexible   B. agile   C. serious   D. svelte   _____

15. We were almost certain to _____ the other team, since we were ahead by twelve points in the last inning.
   A. defeat   B. croquet   C. ascend   D. compete   _____

Exercise 2

Write the letter of the word pair that has a relationship similar to the relationship of the first word pair.

16. *extremely : very : :*   A. paint : can   C. fast : quickly   _____
                             B. sadly : happily   D. slowly : drive

17. *flexible : stiff : :*   A. happy : sad   C. soft : marble   _____
                             B. hungry : food   D. run : fast

18. *compete : competition : :*   A. sad : sadly   C. do : did   _____
                             B. attend : attention   D. sat : sit

19. *defend : goal : :*   A. light : heavy   C. attack : enemy   _____
                             B. dollar : money   D. follow : walk

20. *uniform : body : :*   A. glove : coat   C. shoe : foot   _____
                             B. ring : gold   D. hat : cap

Lesson 3
Performing Arts

All the words in this lesson may be associated with the performing arts.

actress   N. a girl or woman who acts on television, in movies, or on the stage (A girl who is good at pretending to be someone else could make a very good *actress.*)

amateur   N. of or by people doing something for pleasure and not for money (The singer was an *amateur* who loved to perform in her spare time.)

audition   V. to perform as a test (Ballet dancers must *audition* for the director before they are chosen to dance.)

auditorium   N. a large room with a stage and a place for an audience (In the packed *auditorium,* people waited eagerly for the play to begin.)

character   N. person in a play, movie, or book (The main *character* in the movie finally escaped from the burning building.)

climax   N. the most exciting part; the high point of the story (At the play's *climax,* the mad scientist destroyed his secret formula.)

dramatist   N. a writer of plays (A *dramatist* usually enjoys seeing his or her own plays performed on stage.)

hilarious   ADJ. very funny (The show was so *hilarious* that we laughed from start to finish.)

illusion   N. a false notion (The magician created the *illusion* of a rabbit disappearing into a hat.)

impromptu   ADJ. done without prior thought or preparation (Picking topics at random, the drama teacher asked students to stand up and give *impromptu* speeches.)

improvise   V. to make up without preparation (Even when he didn't know a song, the jazz trumpeter could *improvise* as he played with the band.)

mime   V. to act without words (Using only gestures, the clown could *mime* the part of an angry policeman or a happy hunter.)

portray   V. to act the part in a movie or play (Sally was asked to *portray* a beautiful princess in the school play.)

professional   ADJ. receiving payment for skill or performance in sports, arts, or business (We hired a *professional* band to play at the dance.)

puppeteer   N. a person who performs with puppets (After many years of practice, the *puppeteer* learned to move her puppets with ease.)

rehearse   V. to practice for a performance (The director asked us to *rehearse* our parts at home before we met on stage.)

spectator   N. a person who watches (I would rather be a *spectator* in the audience than the concert performer.)

sponsor   N. a person or group who supports (The dancers needed a *sponsor* to pay for their shoes and costumes.)

villain   N. a wicked person (Laughing fiendishly, the *villain* tied the hero's girlfriend to the railroad tracks.)

wings   N. space to the right or left of the stage (The actors exit offstage through the *wings* when the scene ends.)

Exercise 1
Write the letter of the word that best completes the sentence.

1. The actor was only twenty-six, but he created the _____ that he was one hundred _____
years old.
   A. climax   B. illusion   C. audition   D. wings

2. The _____ stood behind the curtain making puppets dance and sing.   _____
   A. actress   B. character   C. puppeteer   D. sponsor

3. Without using props or speaking a word, I had to _____ the part of a man walking   _____
   up stairs.
   A. mime   B. audition   C. improvise   D. rehearse

4. The surprised winner gave a(n) _____ speech when she accepted the award.   _____
   A. amateur   B. hilarious   C. impromptu   D. professional

5. Our teacher made us _____ our play daily so we could learn our parts.   _____
   A. rehearse   B. improvise   C. portray   D. audition

6. When she called the director, the _____ learned she had won the part she wanted.   _____
   A. actress   B. spectator   C. wings   D. villain

7. The drama club needs a _____ to provide support for its shows.   _____
   A. character   B. puppeteer   C. sponsor   D. dramatist

8. More than anything, John wanted to _____ the werewolf in the class play.   _____
   A. improvise   B. audition   C. rehearse   D. portray

9. The _____ magician had never been paid for performing.   _____
   A. amateur   B. impromptu   C. character   D. illusion

10. Sometimes actors must run offstage into the _____ to make costume changes.   _____
    A. climax   B. auditorium   C. sponsor   D. wings

11. In the last scene, Mary forgot what to say and had to _____ her lines.   _____
    A. improvise   B. portray   C. audition   D. mime

12. The movie ending was sad because the most important _____ was killed.   _____
    A. dramatist   B. character   C. spectator   D. wings

13. To become a band member, you must _____ to show how well you play.   _____
    A. mime   B. rehearse   C. portray   D. audition

14. The _____ of the play was so thrilling that I held my breath.   _____
    A. illusion   B. spectator   C. climax   D. dramatist

15. The concert begins just after the lights in the _____ are dimmed.   _____
    A. climax   B. auditorium   C. illusion   D. audition

Exercise 2

Write the letter of the word pair that has a relationship similar to the relationship of the
first word pair.

16. **dramatist : play : :**   A. carpenter : tools   C. driver : car   _____
                                  B. author : book   D. mayor : city

17. **villain : mean : :**   A. policeman : helpful   C. hero : heroine   _____
                                  B. child : adult   D. talented : singer

18. **hilarious : funny : :**   A. friend : enemy   C. empty : jar   _____
                                  B. humorous : tale   D. big : large

19. **spectator : view : :**   A. lawyer : client   C. driver : steer   _____
                                  B. vision : see   D. meadow : flower

20. **professional : money : :** A. ball : bat   C. kindly : soft   _____
                                  B. dollar : dime   D. amateur : free

Lesson 4
Transportation

All the words in this lesson may be associated with transportation.

accelerate   V. to increase speed (The rocket needs to *accelerate* to escape the Earth's gravity.)

carburetor   N. the part of an engine in which fuel is mixed with air so it will burn effectively (The mechanic adjusted the *carburetor* so the car would run more smoothly.)

carload   N. the amount carried by a freight car (It took three trucks to carry away the *carload* of bricks.)

causeway   N. an elevated road (A long *causeway* connected the island to the mainland.)

chauffeur   N. a paid driver (Mr. Leeds instructed his *chauffeur* to drive him to his office.)

circumvent   V. to go around; bypass (To avoid traffic, the new road to the airport will *circumvent* the town.)

collide   V. to crash into (If two cars *collide,* seat belts will dramatically reduce passenger injuries.)

destination   N. the place toward which one is traveling (If we drive all day we will reach our *destination* by dark.)

economical   ADJ. inexpensive; avoiding waste (It is more *economical* to ride in a car pool than to drive in separate cars.)

efficient   ADJ. running with minimal waste (A small car is usually more *efficient* than a large one because it uses less gas.)

haul   V. to cart or transport (The builder must *haul* all the materials to the site before he can begin construction.)

lubricate   V. to apply oil or grease (It is necessary to *lubricate* an engine to keep all the parts moving smoothly.)

mileage   N. the number of miles a car will travel on a gallon of gas (Because the car's *mileage* was low, Joe had to buy gas more often.)

profitable   ADJ. resulting in monetary gain (The route was *profitable* for the airline because there were usually many passengers.)

radiator   N. the cooling system of a car's engine (Always make sure the *radiator* is full of water before a trip so the engine will not overheat.)

rig   N. a large truck with special equipment (The trucker usually leaves his *rig* running at a truck stop.)

suburban   ADJ. lying immediately outside a city (They lived close to the city in a *suburban* area.)

transient   ADJ. temporary; passing through (Motels and hotels provide lodging for *transient* guests.)

various   ADJ. numerous; of many kinds (The bus driver tried out *various* routes in hopes of finding the fastest way to school.)

veer   V. to suddenly change direction (To avoid hitting the cow, the driver had to *veer* into a ditch.)

Exercise 1
Write the letter of the word that best completes the sentence.

1. A trucker's _____ usually includes sleeping quarters.   _____
   A. carburetor   B. causeway   C. rig   D. chauffeur

2. You will _____ with the car in front of you if you don't slow down.   _____
   A. accelerate   B. haul   C. lubricate   D. collide

3. The refrigerated _____ of milk soured when the train broke down.
   A. mileage   B. carload   C. radiator   D. destination   _____

4. The workers had to _____ away the wood after they cut down the tree.
   A. haul   B. veer   C. collide   D. accelerate   _____

5. The city skyline has more tall buildings than the _____ skyline.
   A. transient   B. various   C. suburban   D. economical   _____

6. Your car will have better _____ if you keep the engine tuned.
   A. carburetor   B. mileage   C. destination   D. rig   _____

7. Resort towns are often crowded in summer because of _____ visitors.
   A. efficient   B. economical   C. suburban   D. transient   _____

8. As we approached our _____, we began to recognize familiar landmarks.
   A. rig   B. destination   C. causeway   D. carburetor   _____

9. We watched for alligators as we drove over the _____ that crossed the swamp.
   A. radiator   B. destination   C. causeway   D. rig   _____

10. Ask the mechanic for grease to _____ the engine.
   A. lubricate   B. veer   C. circumvent   D. haul   _____

11. Choose a route that will _____ the stadium on days when a football game is scheduled.
   A. accelerate   B. collide   C. veer   D. circumvent   _____

12. It is important for the _____ to provide the proper mixture of gas and air to the engine.
   A. chauffeur   B. rig   C. carburetor   D. destination   _____

13. Lower expenses will make the new bus route more _____ than the old one.
   A. suburban   B. profitable   C. various   D. transient   _____

14. Try not to _____ sharply when the roads are slippery.
   A. haul   B. circumvent   C. veer   D. lubricate   _____

15. Auto makers try to make engines more _____ to conserve fuel.
   A. efficient   B. suburban   C. various   D. profitable   _____

Exercise 2

Write the letter of the word pair that has a relationship similar to the relationship of the first word pair.

16. *accelerate : speed : :*   A. rocket : orbit   C. drive : car   _____
                               B. grow : height   D. open : door

17. *chauffeur : car : :*   A. chef : food   C. dancer : stage   _____
                               B. athlete : team   D. pilot : airplane

18. *economical : wasteful : :*   A. square : triangle   C. inexpensive : cheap   _____
                               B. real : imaginary   D. tall : heavy

19. *various : variety : :*   A. broken : fixed   C. wintery : winter   _____
                               B. noise : silence   D. large : enormous

20. *radiator : engine : :*   A. ice : beverage   C. shovel : dirt   _____
                               B. switch : light   D. map : road

Lesson 5
Social Studies

All the words in this lesson may be associated with the subject of social studies.

amend   V. to change by adding, removing, or altering (Congress had to *amend* the law to require people to fasten their seat belts.)

ancestor   N. a person from whom one is descended, such as a grandparent or great-grandparent (His mother's *ancestor* sailed to America on the Mayflower.)

barter   V. to trade goods without using money (Pioneer Americans would often *barter* food for tools instead of paying for them.)

compromise   V. to reach an agreement by each side giving something (The two sides finally decided to *compromise* by each giving up one thing it had wanted.)

debate   V. to argue about during a public meeting (In the state house, you can often hear senators' voices as they *debate* an issue for hours.)

discriminate   V. display a difference in treatment (A coffee shop owner cannot *discriminate* against customers because of race.)

frontier   N. an area just beyond a settled region (Many people think that our last *frontier* is outer space.)

institution   N. an organization established for public use (Public schools are *institutions* for learning.)

jury   N. persons chosen to hear evidence in a court of law (The members of the *jury* had to decide whether or not the man was guilty of the crime.)

legislation   N. laws that are made (New *legislation* was created to raise the speed limit on interstate highways.)

manufacture   V. to make by hand or machine (The new factory in town will *manufacture* car parts.)

organize   V. to cause to join together in a union or other group (Factory workers decided to *organize* so that one representative could speak for many people.)

petition   N. a formal request for some right or benefit (We gave the mayor a *petition* asking to use the park for our school carnival.)

politics   N. the science of government (Since George had always been interested in *politics*, I thought he would run for student body president.)

reform   V. make better; improve (Students wanted to *reform* the cafeteria rules to make it easier to sit with friends at lunch.)

resignation   N. the act of quitting a job or position (No one thought my mother would ever quit her job, so her sudden *resignation* was a surprise.)

tariff   N. a tax the government puts on goods coming into the country (The German automobile was expensive because of the high *tariff* on foreign cars.)

truce   N. a stop in fighting (Both sides put down their weapons when a *truce* was declared in the civil war.)

unite   V. combine, join together (The two groups were ready to *unite* and work together to improve the neighborhood.)

volunteer   V. to act of one's own free will (Our teacher asked if someone would *volunteer* to clean the chalkboards.)

Exercise 1
Write the letter of the word that best completes the sentence.

1. We listened to the two senators _____ the problem of gun control.   _____
   A. barter   B. organize   C. debate   D. unite

2. The congress passed _____ making it illegal to drive without wearing a seat belt.   _____
   A. jury   B. frontier   C. politics   D. legislation

3. When a law becomes outdated, our congressmen must _____ it. _____
   A. reform   B. manufacture   C. barter   D. compromise

4. Suzanne learned about an interesting _____ when she read her family history. _____
   A. truce   B. ancestor   C. resignation   D. institution

5. The students sent a(n) _____ to the principal asking for a longer lunch period. _____
   A. jury   B. ancestor   C. petition   D. politics

6. In many small towns, people _____ to act as firemen whenever there is a fire. _____
   A. volunteer   B. debate   C. barter   D. amend

7. The lawyer was asked to _____ the will to include the man's brother. _____
   A. barter   B. discriminate   C. amend   D. volunteer

8. People who enter _____ are interested in the way government works. _____
   A. truce   B. politics   C. institution   D. jury

9. Because he had little money, the farmer would often _____ crops for supplies. _____
   A. amend   B. debate   C. organize   D. barter

10. While settling the new _____, American pioneers faced many hardships. _____
    A. ancestor   B. frontier   C. petition   D. ancestor

11. Members of the class were asked to _____ when they disagreed about a date for
    the class party. _____
    A. amend   B. barter   C. discriminate   D. compromise

12. Older people may find it difficult to get a job because some companies _____
    against them. _____
    A. debate   B. discriminate   C. amend   D. reform

13. Banking is an important _____ in our country. _____
    A. ancestor   B. truce   C. jury   D. institution

14. Concerned families in the neighborhood met to _____ a watch against crime. _____
    A. organize   B. discriminate   C. barter   D. amend

15. The South American company had to pay a(n) _____ on the fruit it imported. _____
    A. ancestor   B. frontier   C. tariff   D. truce

Exercise 2
Write the letter of the word pair that has a relationship similar to the relationship of the
first word pair.

16. **resignation : resign : :**   A. hang : hung   C. red : read   _____
                                     B. action : act   D. invade : invasion

17. **truce : fight : :**   A. stop : start   C. pencil : write   _____
                                     B. small : little   D. clock : time

18. **manufacture : toys : :**   A. fix : repair   C. lantern : lamp   _____
                                     B. house : build   D. cook : food

19. **unite : combine : :**   A. light : dark   C. milk : drink   _____
                                     B. quick : fast   D. dog : bark

20. **jury : people : :**   A. animal : zoo   C. car : truck   _____
                                     B. dancer : practice   D. army : soldiers

Lesson 6
Human Behavior

All the words in this lesson may be associated with human behavior.

cautious   ADJ. very careful, wary (Maria was *cautious* as she skated slowly on the roller blades for the first time.)

ecstatic   ADJ. extremely happy; delighted (The players were *ecstatic* when their team won the championship.)

fiendish   ADJ. wicked; devilish (The wizard cast a *fiendish* spell that turned the princess into a toad.)

flirt   V. to show romantic interest in a light or playful way (Wanda thinks it is fun to *flirt* with boys, but Erica thinks it is a waste of time.)

furtive   ADJ. sneaky or sly (Kurt opened his sister's diary with a *furtive* look.)

gallant   ADJ. dramatically courteous (It was *gallant* of Dion to offer Nancy his seat.)

grouse   V. to complain; grumble (Zach will always *grouse* about his homework.)

heroic   ADJ. very brave and courageous (The firemen made a *heroic* effort to rescue everyone from the burning building.)

honorable   ADJ. honest and fair in one's beliefs and actions (Returning the lost wallet would be the *honorable* thing for Fred to do.)

impetuous   ADJ. acting without thinking about the consequences (She regretted her *impetuous* decision to cut her hair.)

impress   V. to have a strong effect on one's thoughts or feelings (Carlos will *impress* you with his skill on the violin.)

indifferent   ADJ. not caring; having no preference (Because Jeff was not interested in sports, he was *indifferent* about going to the football game.)

mope   V. to sulk or brood (If he does not get his way, he will *mope* in his room until someone cheers him up.)

reckless   ADJ. careless; wild (Bart hurt his arm by being *reckless* on his skateboard.)

relent   V. to become less harsh; to soften (I hope Mother will *relent* and let me go to the sleep over after all.)

seethe   V. to boil inwardly; to be agitated (It made Abbie *seethe* with anger when Amy copied her Halloween costume.)

selfless   ADJ. unselfish (A *selfless* person always has time to do things for others.)

spiteful   ADJ. being mean for petty reasons; revengeful (It was *spiteful* of Lavonne not to invite Rene to her party.)

stingy   ADJ. not wanting to give or spend; not generous (Since my music teacher is *stingy* with her praise, she does not compliment me often.)

worthy   ADJ. having value or excellence (The class made a *worthy* effort to clean up the trash on the playground.)

Exercise 1
Write the letter of the word that best completes the sentence.

1. Even though we were disappointed, we did not sit and _____ when the game was rained out.   _____
   A. flirt   B. mope   C. impress   D. relent

2. Molly thought of a(n) _____ trick to play on her brother on April Fool's Day.   _____
   A. fiendish   B. stingy   C. ecstatic   D. indifferent

3. The teacher was sure that a tour of the nuclear reactor would _____ the class.   _____
   A. flirt   B. mope   C. impress   D. relent

4. The soldier won a medal for his _____ action in battle.   _____
   A. stingy   B. heroic   C. furtive   D. spiteful

5. I hope the gym teacher will _____ and not make us do fifty push-ups.   _____
   A. impress   B. mope   C. seethe   D. relent

6. David likes to _____ with Lin-ye by sending her silly little notes.   _____
   A. seethe   B. relent   C. flirt   D. grouse

7. The committee felt Andy's essay was _____ of second prize.   _____
   A. indifferent   B. worthy   C. fiendish   D. stingy

8. Even though Marty likes to _____ about the school lunch, he always finishes   _____
   everything on his plate.
   A. grouse   B. impress   C. relent   D. flirt

9. Because he was feeling _____, Marcus held the door open for the whole class.   _____
   A. stingy   B. fiendish   C. indifferent   D. gallant

10. The yearly talent show made the class _____ with excitement.   _____
    A. flirt   B. impress   C. seethe   D. mope

Exercise 2

Write the letter of the word that most nearly has the *opposite* meaning of the italicized
word.

11. *spiteful*	A. nervous	B. kind	C. silly	D. moody	_____
12. *indifferent*	A. difficult	B. wild	C. angry	D. eager	_____
13. *ecstatic*	A. sad	B. crafty	C. nice	D. dazed	_____
14. *cautious*	A. loud	B. careless	C. lazy	D. smart	_____
15. *honorable*	A. hungry	B. awake	C. dishonest	D. poor	_____
16. *stingy*	A. unselfish	B. stupid	C. quick	D. excellent	_____
17. *impetuous*	A. different	B. loyal	C. boastful	D. planned	_____
18. *selfless*	A. sudden	B. fair	C. greedy	D. friendly	_____
19. *reckless*	A. snobbish	B. careful	C. private	D. mean	_____
20. *furtive*	A. handy	B. successful	C. joking	D. open	_____

Lesson 7
Human Behavior

All the words in this lesson may be associated with human behavior.

affectionate   ADJ. loving, fond (Paul gave his aunt an *affectionate* hug.)

agreeable   ADJ. willing; ready to go along with (Our teacher was *agreeable* to postponing the test.)

ambitious   ADJ. eager to achieve or excel (The after-school math workshop is for *ambitious* students.)

ardent   ADJ. expressing intense feeling; passionate (The Conservation Club wrote an *ardent* letter in support of the recycling program.)

authoritative   ADJ. acting as if in command (With an *authoritative* manner, William directed the younger students to their classes on the first day of school.)

barbaric   ADJ. uncivilized; rude (I like to tease my brother about his *barbaric* table manners.)

candid   ADJ. frank; honest (Don't try to spare my feelings, just give me your *candid* opinion of these poems.)

confident   ADJ. sure of oneself (Because she had worked hard, Meghan felt *confident* before the track meet.)

considerate   ADJ. concerned about the feelings of others; kind (It is not *considerate* to talk and laugh loudly in the library.)

cooperative   ADJ. willing to work together (Because of our *cooperative* attitude, our group had few disagreements during the project.)

courtly   ADJ. elegant; very polite (Max gave Latasha a *courtly* bow when he invited her to the prom.)

diplomatic   ADJ. avoiding hurting others; tactful (Josh tried to think of a *diplomatic* way to tell his mother he did not like the shirt.)

disagreeable   ADJ. unpleasant; unfriendly (My friends tell me to go to bed on time because I am very *disagreeable* when I am tired.)

distracted   ADJ. having one's attention drawn away (Ben lost his place in his book when he was *distracted* by sirens in the street.)

enthusiastic   ADJ. very eager; wholehearted (The *enthusiastic* applause showed that the audience had enjoyed the concert.)

fretful   ADJ. irritable; cranky (Babies often become *fretful* when they are hungry.)

haughty   ADJ. overly proud or snobbish (The winner's *haughty* attitude made her unpopular with the other swimmers.)

impeccable   ADJ. flawless (There was not a single wrong note in Mike's *impeccable* performance at the concert.)

preoccupied   ADJ. not paying attention because one is lost in thought (Wendy is *preoccupied* with worry because her puppy is sick.)

restless   ADJ. unable to keep still (Hoping the play would be over soon, the *restless* child squirmed in her seat.)

Exercise 1
Write the letter of the word that best completes the sentence.

1. Because he is easily _____, Mark needs a quiet place to do his homework.   _____
   A. impeccable   B. fretful   C. confident   D. distracted

2. The cruel prince gave the beggar a(n) _____ look and turned his back.   _____
   A. affectionate   B. haughty   C. cooperative   D. considerate

3. My uncle loves softball, and he is a(n) _____ fan of the local team.   _____
   A. ardent   B. diplomatic   C. fretful   D. barbaric

4. The king helped the queen into her velvet cloak with a(n) _____ gesture.   _____
   A. candid   B. courtly   C. ambitious   D. fretful

5. It is _____ to offer your seat on a bus to an elderly passenger.   _____
   A. fretful   B. ardent   C. considerate   D. distracted

6. Rob did a(n) _____ job of drawing all the details of the electronics board.   _____
   A. disagreeable   B. haughty   C. preoccupied   D. impeccable

7. The candidate with the most _____ manner was chosen to lead the party.   _____
   A. authoritative   B. barbaric   C. affectionate   D. distracted

8. Because his comments are always _____, I trust Bill's opinion.   _____
   A. barbaric   B. ardent   C. candid   D. courtly

9. Dion is usually so cheerful that it is surprising to see him in such a(n) _____
   mood.   _____
   A. ambitious   B. disagreeable   C. courtly   D. cooperative

10. The children are becoming _____ at having to wait so long for the parade to start.   _____
   A. affectionate   B. enthusiastic   C. agreeable   D. restless

Exercise 2
Write the letter of the word that most nearly has the *opposite* meaning of the italicized word.

11. *diplomatic*   A. unkind   B. calm   C. angry   D. foreign   _____

12. *fretful*   A. active   B. happy   C. mature   D. moody   _____

13. *preoccupied*   A. proud   B. sad   C. talkative   D. alert   _____

14. *barbaric*   A. joyful   B. crude   C. polite   D. quiet   _____

15. *cooperative*   A. selfish   B. eager   C. helpful   D. scared   _____

16. *ambitious*   A. worried   B. annoyed   C. lazy   D. cruel   _____

17. *enthusiastic*   A. confused   B. unconcerned   C. excited   D. silly   _____

18. *agreeable*   A. willing   B. busy   C. calm   D. opposed   _____

19. *confident*   A. odd   B. rude   C. shy   D. loud   _____

20. *affectionate*   A. uncaring   B. clumsy   C. sly   D. nervous   _____

Lesson 8
The Desert

All the words in this lesson may be associated with the desert.

absorb   V. to soak up or take in (A cactus will *absorb* water from the ground or the air and store it in its thick stem.)

destruction   N. great damage or ruin (Heavy rains filled the river beds and caused the *destruction* of many bridges.)

drought   N. a long period of no rain; very dry weather (By August, the long *drought* had made the meadow look brown and dry.)

cacti   N. plural form of cactus, a desert plant with sharp spines or thorns. (Many *cacti* bloomed in the desert after the spring rains.)

cluster   N. items of the same kind that are grouped or that grow together (There were five blossoms in each *cluster* of cactus flowers.)

erode   V. to wear away gradually (When there is no moisture in the ground, the wind can *erode* the soil by blowing away the dusty top layer of dirt.)

evaporate   V. to change from a liquid or a solid into a gas (A puddle of rain water in the desert will *evaporate* quickly and leave the ground dry and hard.)

extract   V. to take out or pull out (The doctor had to use tweezers to *extract* the cactus thorn from the boy's finger.)

frugal   ADJ. using things wisely; not wasteful (He was *frugal* with his water on the hike and only drank small amounts when he was thirsty.)

precipitation   N. moisture in the form of rain or snow (Because there is very little *precipitation* in the desert, only plants that will grow in dry soil can survive.)

prey   N. an animal hunted by another animal for food (Catching the rabbit in its jaws, the desert fox began to eat its *prey*.)

prickly   ADJ. having many sharp points or thorns (People who touch a *prickly* cactus are often scratched by thorns.)

protect   V. guard from harm or danger (We must *protect* the beauty of our deserts for future generations to enjoy.)

pulpy   ADJ. spongy and moist (He chewed the *pulpy* inside of the cactus stem to squeeze out the liquid that it held.)

spines   N. sharp, pointed growth on a plant or animal (Most animals will not eat a cactus because of the sharp *spines* that cover the plant.)

swoop   V. to sweep down upon in a sudden attack (The great horned owl will *swoop* down from the sky to catch small mice on the ground.)

topsoil   N. the top or upper part of the soil (Many small plants grow in the sandy *topsoil* of the desert.)

unusual   ADJ. uncommon; not ordinary (Desert plants and wildlife may seem *unusual* to people who live in the Midwest.)

variety   N. a number of different kinds (The desert supports many types of plants along with a large *variety* of wildlife.)

vegetation   N. plant life (The desert has very little *vegetation* because few plants will grow where it is so dry.)

Exercise 1
Write the letter of the word that best completes the sentence.

1. The hungry coyote chased its _____ through the hot desert.   _____
   A. cacti   B. prey   C. destruction   D. spines

2. Heavy rains caused the river banks to _____ and wash away.   _____
   A. absorb   B. evaporate   C. swoop   D. erode

3. Because of the _____, water was scarce and the animals became thirsty. _____
   A. spines   B. drought   C. topsoil   D. vegetation

4. Hikers watched the hawk _____ down and snatch the jackrabbit in its claws. _____
   A. swoop   B. evaporate   C. protect   D. absorb

5. In spring, you see many different colors in the desert because of the great _____ _____
of wild flowers.
   A. topsoil   B. cacti   C. variety   D. destruction

6. Because we were _____ during the winter, we were able to save enough money _____
for our desert trip.
   A. prickly   B. unusual   C. pulpy   D. frugal

7. Water will not _____ if it is stored in a canteen. _____
   A. evaporate   B. absorb   C. erode   D. extract

8. Some plants can _____ water in the air through their leaves. _____
   A. swoop   B. protect   C. absorb   D. erode

9. The scientists examined the desert _____ looking for signs of plant life. _____
   A. cacti   B. topsoil   C. drought   D. variety

10. When the _____ are all in bloom, the desert is a colorful place. _____
   A. prey   B. topsoil   C. spines   D. cacti

Exercise 2

Write the letter of the word that most nearly has the *same* meaning as the italicized word.

11. *prickly*	A. sharp	B. smooth	C. dull	D. loud	_____
12. *precipitation*	A. wind	B. growth	C. rain	D. noise	_____
13. *destruction*	A. heat	B. solution	C. filling	D. wreck	_____
14. *vegetation*	A. weather	B. plants	C. soil	D. animals	_____
15. *pulpy*	A. thin	B. long	C. sharp	D. soft	_____
16. *unusual*	A. common	B. small	C. bare	D. rare	_____
17. *cluster*	A. group	B. fence	C. flower	D. weed	_____
18. *spines*	A. stems	B. thorns	C. twigs	D. trees	_____
19. *extract*	A. add	B. bite	C. remove	D. improve	_____
20. *protect*	A. guard	B. bite	C. run	D. waste	_____

Lesson 9
Geography

All the words in this lesson may be associated with geography.

adapt   V. to adjust to new conditions (People moving to another country *adapt* to a new way of life by learning new customs.)

arable   ADJ. suitable for planting (The farmer decided that the rocky soil was not *arable* land.)

barren   ADJ. unable to produce anything (Nothing grew in the *barren* field.)

contour   N. outline of a figure; shape (The *contour* of Italy is similar to that of a boot.)

cultivate   V. to prepare and use land to raise crops (Farmers use plows to *cultivate* the land in the spring.)

deciduous   ADJ. shedding leaves at the end of a growing season (Elms and maples lose their leaves in the fall because they are *deciduous* trees.)

dense   ADJ. close together, thick (It was difficult to walk through the *dense* undergrowth in the forest.)

devastate   V. destroy, ruin (A hurricane can *devastate* land and people by wrecking buildings and flooding cities.)

diverse   ADJ. varied, different (There were people from many countries in the city's *diverse* population.)

famine   N. having no food; time of starving (During the *famine* in Ethiopia, thousands of children died from hunger.)

fault   N. a break in the earth's crust (The *fault* caused by the earthquake looked like a crack in the ground.)

foliage   N. leaves of a plant; greenery (The tree's *foliage* made the yard shady in summer.)

import   V. to bring in from another country for sale (Because it is difficult to grow bananas in the United States, we must *import* them from South and Central America.)

irrigate   V. to water farm land with a system of ditches or by using sprinklers (Where there is little rain, farmers must *irrigate* their crops.)

metropolitan   ADJ. of a large city (There are many large office buildings and stores in a *metropolitan* area.)

precipice   N. a very steep face of a rock; cliff (The rock climber looked over the edge of the *precipice* and saw the valley far below.)

residential   ADJ. having to do with homes or houses (Although the business district of the town was crowded and noisy, the neighborhoods in the *residential* section were quiet and peaceful.)

semiarid   ADJ. having little rainfall (Although there was some rain, the *semiarid* climate at the edge of the desert was not good for growing crops.)

survey   V. to measure for size, shape, and boundaries (The highway department had to *survey* the land before constructing the new road.)

tributary   N. a stream or river that flows into a larger body of water (The Wisconsin River is a *tributary* of the Mississippi.)

Exercise 1
Write the letter of the word that best completes the sentence.

1. We paddled our canoe down a small _____ until we reached the big river. _____
   A. famine   B. tributary   C. precipice   D. fault

2. There is not much _____ land in the high mountains because the soil is thin. _____
   A. deciduous   B. semiarid   C. barren   D. arable

3. Have someone _____ your land to determine the boundaries.   _____
   A. import   B. devastate   C. survey   D. cultivate

4. Some scientists believe that dinosaurs became extinct because they could not   _____
   _____ to the changing environment.
   A. adapt   B. cultivate   C. import   D. survey

5. The _____ of the California coast is very jagged.   _____
   A. foliage   B. famine   C. contour   D. tributary

6. Because my father liked having neighbors, he chose to live in a(n) _____ area.   _____
   A. residential   B. barren   C. deciduous   D. arable

7. In autumn, the leaves of some _____ trees turn red.   _____
   A. barren   B. deciduous   C. arable   D. semiarid

8. Because of the poor harvest, the country had to _____ grain.   _____
   A. adapt   B. survey   C. import   D. devastate

9. The farmer used the water from the river to _____ his land.   _____
   A. irrigate   B. survey   C. adapt   D. import

10. The _____ was too steep to climb, so the hikers took an alternate route.   _____
    A. fault   B. precipice   C. contour   D. tributary

Exercise 2

Write the letter of the word that most nearly has the *same* meaning of the italicized word.

11. *cultivate*	A. climb	B. ruin	C. plow	D. wash	_____
12. *diverse*	A. various	B. huge	C. similar	D. shiny	_____
13. *barren*	A. red	B. fruitless	C. high	D. hungry	_____
14. *semiarid*	A. dry	B. crowded	C. windy	D. quiet	_____
15. *metropolitan*	A. slow	B. cluttered	C. urban	D. wet	_____
16. *dense*	A. heavy	B. green	C. thick	D. sparse	_____
17. *fault*	A. crack	B. trail	C. lake	D. signal	_____
18. *famine*	A. city	B. cry	C. opening	D. hunger	_____
19. *foliage*	A. leaves	B. bark	C. roots	D. branches	_____
20. *devastate*	A. work	B. move	C. destroy	D. build	_____

Lesson 10
Feelings

All the words in this lesson may be associated with feelings.

alarm   V. to frighten (The stranger did not mean to *alarm* the man by knocking on the window.)

annoy   V. to bother or disturb (The constant barking of my neighbor's dog began to *annoy* me.)

baffle   V. to confuse (Bewildering clues in the case continued to *baffle* the detective.)

blissful   ADJ. happy; joyful (Everything was perfect during the newlyweds' *blissful* honeymoon.)

content   ADJ. pleased; satisfied (After a hard day's work, the woman was *content* to sit at home and read.)

cowardly   ADJ. lacking courage (The *cowardly* lion ran when he saw a mouse.)

delight   V. to give great joy or pleasure (The children loved to watch the magician who would *delight* them with his feats of magic.)

dreadful   ADJ. very terrible or frightening (Anna had a *dreadful* feeling that she would be chosen next to play at the recital.)

elated   ADJ. extremely happy (The father was *elated* when his son made the honor roll.)

gloomy   ADJ. sad; in low spirits (Everyone felt *gloomy* and discouraged during the week of rainy weather at the beach.)

harsh   ADJ. very cruel (The sailors could expect *harsh* treatment from the unfeeling captain.)

hospitable   ADJ. giving friendly and welcoming treatment (Meeting the guests with a smile, the *hospitable* hotel manager made sure that everyone was comfortable.)

listless   ADJ. lacking in energy or spirit (During the hot afternoon, she felt *listless* and did not want to do anything that required any effort.)

meek   ADJ. easily ordered around by others; not showing determination (The boy was so *meek* that he would not stand up for his own rights.)

nasty   ADJ. mean or spiteful (Throwing rocks at the neighbor's dog was a *nasty* thing to do.)

optimistic   ADJ. looking on the bright side of things (After an encouraging talk with her boss, Laura felt *optimistic* about getting a pay raise.)

provoke   V. to make angry (If the students continue to misbehave, they will *provoke* the teacher and she will cancel recess.)

sympathetic   ADJ. showing kindness and pity towards others (The *sympathetic* neighbor brought flowers to the sick woman.)

tense   ADJ. strained or tight (Many speakers feel *tense* and nervous before stepping in front of a crowd.)

uneasy   ADJ. worried and nervous (Although John's mother told him he could go to the dance, she felt *uneasy* about his staying out so late.)

Exercise 1
Write the letter of the word that best completes the sentence.

1. After his illness, the boy felt _____ and tired.   _____
   A. elated   B. nasty   C. harsh   D. listless

2. These confusing directions will _____ the students.   _____
   A. baffle   B. delight   C. alarm   D. provoke

3. The fly buzzing around her head began to _____ Jean as she studied for her test.   _____
   A. alarm   B. annoy   C. baffle   D. delight

4. The _____ child was sent home after kicking other children.   _____
   A. nasty   B. delighted   C. optimistic   D. meek

5. Ellen was a _____ friend who always tried to understand her friends' problems.   _____
   A. cowardly   B. blissful   C. harsh   D. sympathetic

6. The musicians at the cafe will _____ you with their happy songs.   _____
   A. delight   B. provoke   C. alarm   D. baffle

7. Although he could have changed to a smaller class, Arthur was _____ to stay in   _____
   the larger one.
   A. meek   B. uneasy   C. content   D. dreadful

8. After flying through the bad storm, the passengers were happy to end the _____   _____
   flight.
   A. blissful   B. cowardly   C. dreadful   D. nasty

9. Because he was afraid to come without his homework finished, the _____ boy   _____
   stayed home from school.
   A. optimistic   B. cowardly   C. elated   D. harsh

10. The team was _____ when it won the state championship.   _____
    A. listless   B. meek   C. elated   D. gloomy

Exercise 2
Write the letter of the word that most nearly has the *opposite* meaning as the italicized
word.

11. *provoke*	A. encourage	B. simplify	C. pat	D. calm	_____
12. *hospitable*	A. unfriendly	B. sick	C. satisfied	D. helpful	_____
13. *optimistic*	A. mild	B. funny	C. down	D. angry	_____
14. *blissful*	A. hurt	B. rude	C. sad	D. glad	_____
15. *tense*	A. relaxed	B. neat	C. shy	D. tired	_____
16. *harsh*	A. upset	B. energetic	C. hopeful	D. kind	_____
17. *uneasy*	A. lucky	B. comfortable	C. cold	D. silly	_____
18. *alarm*	A. ride	B. test	C. force	D. calm	_____
19. *meek*	A. pleased	B. soft	C. strong	D. silent	_____
20. *gloomy*	A. gentle	B. sour	C. cheerful	D. honest	_____

Lesson 11
Outer Space

All the words in this lesson may be associated with outer space.

adrift   ADJ. without direction or anchor (The garbage thrown from the space ship was *adrift* in space and floated slowly past the ship's window.)

asteroid   N. one of many rocky bodies that revolve around the sun (The spaceship photographed an *asteroid* between the orbits of Mars and Jupiter.)

astronomer   N. a scientist who studies the sun, moon, planets, and stars (Gazing through the telescope, the *astronomer* saw the craters on the moon's surface.)

biosphere   N. the part of the earth that supports life (Plants and animals cannot live outside the earth's *biosphere* because of the lack of oxygen and water.)

celestial   ADJ. of the sky or heavens (The stars and planets are *celestial* bodies.)

diameter   N. the distance from one side of a circle or sphere to the other through the center (The *diameter* of the earth is close to 8,000 miles.)

diffuse   V. to spread out and cover a large area (As the sun shines on the earth, light and heat will *diffuse* over the earth's surface.)

elliptical   ADJ. shaped like an oval (The earth orbits the sun in an *elliptical* path.)

envision   V. to picture in your mind (Science fiction writers can help you *envision* life on other planets.)

existence   N. a state of being or existing (Until the planet Pluto was discovered in 1930, no one knew of its *existence*.)

extraterrestrial   ADJ. beyond or outside the earth (Scientists launch rocket ships to study *extraterrestrial* space.)

galaxy   N. billions of stars in a group that form one system (Earth is only one tiny part of the *galaxy* called the Milky Way.)

gravitate   V. to move towards a body by force of gravity (The distance from Earth to the sun changes slightly because all planets *gravitate* towards the sun.)

lunar   ADJ. of the moon (Through the telescope you could see the *lunar* satellite orbiting the moon.)

meteorite   N. a piece of stone or metal that comes from space and falls through Earth's atmosphere (When the *meteorite* fell into the field, it left a deep hole.)

observatory   N. a building with a telescope for observing stars and other heavenly bodies (Astronomy students spend time at the *observatory* studying the planets.)

reflect   V. to throw back light, heat, or sound (When we see one entire side of the moon *reflect* sunlight, we say the moon is full.)

revolve   V. to move around a central point (The planets of the solar system *revolve* around the sun.)

shuttle   N. a vehicle that runs back and forth over a distance (A space *shuttle* can go into space and return to earth many times.)

solar   ADJ. of the sun (Some people store heat from sunlight and use the *solar* energy to warm their houses instead of using electricity or gas.)

Exercise 1
Write the letter of the word that best completes the sentence.

1. Because it had no power, the broken space ship was _____ in outer space.   _____
   A. elliptical   B. adrift   C. solar   D. celestial

2. A comet may _____ toward a planet as it passes by.   _____
   A. gravitate   B. diffuse   C. reflect   D. astronomer

3. The _____ gave a lecture about two newly discovered stars.   _____
   A. biosphere   B. galaxy   C. shuttle   D. astronomer

4. After orbiting for three days, the space _____ was ready to return to earth.   _____
   A. observatory   B. biosphere   C. shuttle   D. existence

5. It is difficult to imagine, but if you try, you can _____ what it would be like to live on   _____
   the moon.
   A. envision   B. gravitate   C. diffuse   D. revolve

6. If you multiply the _____ of the Earth by 3.1416, you will find the distance around   _____
   the earth at the equator.
   A. existence   B. asteroid   C. diameter   D. shuttle

7. You begin to leave the Earth's _____ when you reach an altitude of 1000 miles.   _____
   A. biosphere   B. observatory   C. meteorite   D. asteroid

8. At the _____ we looked at stars and planets through a telescope.   _____
   A. galaxy   B. biosphere   C. diameter   D. observatory

9. The moons of Jupiter _____ around the giant planet.   _____
   A. diffuse   B. revolve   C. reflect   D. gravitate

10. Young children often believe in the _____ of " the man on the moon."   _____
    A. existence   B. galaxy   C. diameter   D. biosphere

11. Many moon rock samples were collected during _____ explorations.   _____
    A. lunar   B. adrift   C. solar   D. elliptical

12. The size of the _____ was small compared to the size of the earth.   _____
    A. galaxy   B. existence   C. biosphere   D. asteroid

13. She held her calculator up to the light because it used _____ power instead of   _____
    batteries.
    A. celestial   B. lunar   C. solar   D. adrift

14. Long ago people thought that the stars and other _____ bodies moved around the   _____
    earth.
    A. elliptical   B. adrift   C. lunar   D. celestial

15. The smooth surface of the pond will _____ the sun's rays just like a mirror.   _____
    A. reflect   B. revolve   C. gravitate   D. envision

Exercise 2

Write the letter of the word pair that has a relationship similar to the relationship of the
first word pair.

16. *meteorite : metal : :*   A. dog : bark   C. win : lose   _____
                                 B. shoe : leather   D. wrist : hand

17. *diffuse : spread : :*   A. life : death   C. blue : color   _____
                                 B. glass : break   D. close : shut

18. *galaxy : stars : :*   A. book : pages   C. water : ship   _____
                                 B. sun : bright   D. open : shut

19. *elliptical : circle : :*   A. inches : ruler   C. length : feet   _____
                                 B. end : begin   D. rectangular : square

20. *extraterrestrial : earthly : :*   A. soap : clean   C. bird : sky   _____
                                       B. snow : cold   D. new : old

Lesson 12
Science

All the words in this lesson may be associated with the field of science.

approximate   ADJ. almost correct (On the scale, the chemical weighed exactly 994 grams, so its *approximate* weight was about 1 kilogram.)

automatic   ADJ. moving by itself (Before *automatic* wipers were invented, people had to wipe off the car's windshield by hand.)

biologist   N. a scientist who studies plants and animals (The *biologist* spent many years studying algae and mosquitos in the swamp.)

carcinogen   N. any substance that causes cancer (A food product that contains a *carcinogen* will be banned by the government.)

carrier   N. a person or animal that *carries* or spreads a disease (If you are bitten by a mosquito that is a *carrier* of malaria, you will probably get sick.)

condense   V. to change from a vapor or gas to a liquid (Steam from a teapot will *condense* on the sides of a cold glass and form tiny drops of water.)

conserve   V. to keep from being used up (Scientists tell us to *conserve* oil and natural gas, because supplies are limited.)

deficiency   N. lack of something needed (Bones may become soft if there is a *deficiency* of calcium in a person's diet.)

dissect   V. to cut apart for the purposes of study (The scientist used a sharp knife to *dissect* the fish and look for the cause of death.)

geologist   N. a scientist who studies the earth's crust (The *geologist* gathered rock samples in the Grand Canyon.)

immune   ADJ. protected from disease (The girl would not get the measles because the shot had made her *immune* to the disease.)

microscopic   ADJ. not able to be seen without a microscope (The *microscopic* plants could be seen when they were magnified many times.)

opaque   ADJ. not letting light through (The cage was made of *opaque* material so the rats could not tell if it was day or night.)

painstaking   ADJ. very careful (The scientist never hurried, but conducted her experiments in a *painstaking* manner.)

porous   ADJ. full of tiny holes which allow water and air to pass (Steel is not a *porous* substance.)

research   N. careful investigation or study (When the team of scientists had completed their *research,* they wrote a journal article about what they had learned.)

resistance   N. the act of fighting against (Some insects are no longer affected by insect poisons because they have developed a *resistance* to them.)

retest   V. to test or evaluate again (Because he was uncertain about the results of his experiments on rats, he decided to *retest* the animals.)

soluble   ADJ. able to be dissolved (Sugar is *soluble* in water.)

theory   N. an explanation based on observation and reasoning instead of proof (After watching the movements of the planets for many years, Galileo developed a *theory* about the design of the solar system.)

Exercise 1
Write the letter of the word that best completes the sentence.

1. A sponge is made of a(n) _____ material.   _____
   A. soluble   B. automatic   C. immune   D. porous

2. The scientist found that the results of his radar experiments supported his _____   _____
   about the causes of sunspots.
   A. theory   B. carrier   C. deficiency   D. carcinogen

3. You can be a _____ of a genetic disease, and not be sick yourself.   _____
   A. resistance   B. theory   C. carrier   D. geologist

4. The operating room door had a(n) _____ opener so doctors did not have to touch   _____
   the door to enter.
   A. immune   B. soluble   C. automatic   D. approximate

5. The student became ill watching his lab partner _____ the frog.   _____
   A. dissect   B. condense   C. retest   D. approximate

6. The teacher had to _____ some students because they had failed the exam.   _____
   A. dissect   B. approximate   C. retest   D. condense

7. The laboratory door was _____, and we could not tell if the lights were on.   _____
   A. immune   B. microscopic   C. porous   D. opaque

8. The _____ temperature of the liquid was about 90 degrees centigrade.   _____
   A. approximate   B. immune   C. porous   D. automatic

9. Once you have had smallpox, you are _____ to the disease.   _____
   A. opaque   B. immune   C. porous   D. microscopic

10. The powder and alcohol would not mix because the powder was not _____ in   _____
    alcohol.
    A. painstaking   B. opaque   C. soluble   D. automatic

11. Medical _____ tries to find ways to cure diseases.   _____
    A. resistance   B. geology   C. deficiency   D. research

12. A _____ is dangerous to your health and should be avoided.   _____
    A. geologist   B. theory   C. carcinogen   D. biologist

13. Young children often have a low _____ to colds.   _____
    A. resistance   B. carrier   C. theory   D. deficiency

14. He watched the warm air _____ on the cold window.   _____
    A. retest   B. condense   C. dissect   D. conserve

15. Because of her iron _____ , the doctor prescribed daily vitamins with iron.   _____
    A. biologist   B. deficiency   C. theory   D. carrier

Exercise 2

Write the letter of the word pair that has a relationship similar to the relationship of the
first word pair.

16. *geologist : geology : :*   A. rock : hard   C. build : make   _____
                                   B. engine : go   D. historian : history

17. *painstaking : careful : :*   A. small : tiny   C. three : four   _____
                                   B. many : few   D. dog : bark

18. *biologist : microscope : :*   A. glove : hand   C. girl : mother   _____
                                   B. carpenter : hammer   D. more : less

19. *conserve : waste : :*   A. help : hurt   C. ear : hear   _____
                                   B. story : song   D. end : finish

20. *microscopic : cell : :*   A. small : little   C. huge : mountain   _____
                                   B. length : width   D. win : lose

Lesson 13
Earth Science

All the words in this lesson may be associated with the field of earth science.

bedrock N. the solid rock layer under soil and gravel (The oil company will drill through *bedrock* in its search for new oil wells.)

butte N. an isolated hill that rises suddenly from surrounding flat land (From the top of the *butte* you could see the plains stretching for miles in every direction.)

deposit N. an area in which a great amount of one type of rock or mineral occurs (The miners were sure that there was a rich *deposit* of gold in the mountains.)

elevation N. the height above sea level (The map indicated the *elevation* of different areas by changes in color.)

environment N. the surroundings in which a plant or animal lives (When houses were built in the wetlands, the *environment* of the water birds changed.)

eruption N. the process of emerging violently from within the earth (The volcano's *eruption* threw molten lava into the air.)

fossil N. the traces or imprint of a plant or animal that lived many years ago (In the piece of rock, the *fossil* of the prehistoric dragonfly showed a clear outline of the insect's body.)

geyser N. a hot spring that sprays water and steam into the air (Old Faithful is a famous *geyser* in Yellowstone Park.)

glacier N. a huge mass of slowly moving ice (An iceberg is a chunk of a *glacier* that breaks off and floats in the sea.)

mercury N. the only metal that is a liquid at room temperature (In a thermometer, heat makes a column of *mercury* rise.)

ore N. a type of rock that contains enough of a more valuable metal or mineral to make it worth mining (Aluminum is obtained from an *ore* called bauxite.)

phenomena N. events that can be observed and studied (Hurricanes and tornadoes are among the *phenomena* that interest meteorologists.)

pinnacle N. a high peak (The climbers reached the *pinnacle* of the mountain.)

prospector N. one who looks for valuable metals and minerals (The *prospector* chipped off samples of rock as he searched for silver.)

specimen N. a sample of a material taken for study (The laboratory received a *specimen* of moon rocks to analyze.)

strata N. layers (Scientists have found that where there are several *strata* of rock; the oldest layer is on the bottom and the newest layer is on top.)

topography N. the surface features of the earth, such as mountains, valleys, and rivers (She knew there were no hills in the area because she had studied the *topography* of the region.)

turf N. the top layer of soil that is held together by grass (The thick *turf* that grew over the fossil beds made digging difficult.)

uranium N. a white radioactive metal (*Uranium* is an element used in atomic bombs.)

vicinity N. the area nearby (Because there are so many interesting rock formations in the *vicinity*, scientists often come here to study.)

Exercise 1
Write the letter of the word that best completes the sentence.

1. When digging the basement for the new building, workers found a _____ of a   _____
   dinosaur bone.
   A. turf   B. butte   C. fossil   D. vicinity

2. Although it acts like a liquid, _____ is really a metal.   _____
   A. mercury   B. turf   C. elevation   D. uranium

3. With no mountains nearby, the _____ looks dramatic as it rises from the plain.
   A. specimen   B. bedrock   C. prospector   D. butte
   _____

4. Every afternoon, the _____shoots a huge plume of steam high into the air.
   A. topography   B. environment   C. geyser   D. ore
   _____

5. They used a plow to break up the _____ where the garden was planned.
   A. butte   B. turf   C. pinnacle   D. mercury
   _____

6. A less expensive way was found to separate the silver from the _____ at the mine.
   A. eruption   B. elevation   C. glacier   D. ore
   _____

7. The geologist brought a _____ of the rock back to the laboratory to examine.
   A. specimen   B. pinnacle   C. butte   D. fault
   _____

8. The engineers will have to study the effect the dam will have on the _____.
   A. glacier   B. environment   C. phenomena   D. uranium
   _____

9. There is no clue from the _____ that a huge cave lies under the area.
   A. deposit   B. prospector   C. topography   D. butte
   _____

10. The mountain's _____ was 860 feet above sea level.
   A. vicinity   B. geyser   C. turf   D. elevation
   _____

11. Special precautions are needed when working with radioactive _____.
   A. bedrock   B. uranium   C. pinnacle   D. mercury
   _____

12. On his map, the prospector marked the location of the rich _____ of gold.
   A. deposit   B. butte   C. glacier   D. geyser
   _____

13. The _____ had been predicted, so the people near the volcano left in time.
   A. strata   B. specimen   C. eruption   D. bedrock
   _____

14. The mountain's _____ was the highest point in the range.
   A. geyser   B. pinnacle   C. environment   D. bedrock
   _____

15. In cold weather, birds flocked to the _____ of the hot springs.
   A. strata   B. elevation   C. uranium   D. vicinity
   _____

Exercise 2

Write the letter of the word pair that has a relationship similar to the relationship of the first word pair.

16. *fossil : rock : :*   A. up : down   C. car : driver
                                B. rain : mist   D. footprint : mud
   _____

17. *bedrock : soil : :*   A. star : moon   C. car : highway
                                B. floor : rug   D. height : weight
   _____

18. *glacier : ice : :*   A. sidewalk : concrete C. dish : table
                                B. sad : happy   D. plant : field
   _____

19. *phenomena : events : :*   A. cat : dog   C. car : auto
                                B. king : subject   D. glasses : see
   _____

20. *prospector : gold : :*   A. horn : band   C. actor : actress
                                B. detective : clues   D. wet : dry
   _____

Lesson 14
Aviation

All the words in this lesson may be associated with the field of aviation.

abrupt   ADJ. sudden (We all lurched forward as the plane made an *abrupt* stop.)

aerial   ADJ. in or from the air (From the balloon, the passengers got an *aerial* view of the city.)

altitude   N. height above ground (The plane climbed to an *altitude* of 28,000 feet.)

cargo   N. freight carried by an airplane (The plane's *cargo* consisted of two bags of mail and a crate of oranges.)

cockpit   N. the front part of an airplane where the pilot sits (The pilot and the copilot sat in the *cockpit* and prepared the plane for take-off.)

commercial   ADJ. having to do with business (Since the soldier couldn't get a flight on a military plane, he had to pay full price on a *commercial* flight.)

decrease   V. to make less; to lower (The speed of the plane will *decrease* as it comes in for a landing.)

descend   V. to go down from a higher to a lower place (The airliner began to *descend* from 25,000 feet to land in Chicago.)

hangar   N. a building used for storing or repairing airplanes (The pilot left his plane in the *hangar* so it could be cleaned and checked.)

maintenance   N. the action of keeping in good condition or preserving (Proper *maintenance* of the aircraft includes oiling the engine parts.)

navigate   V. to steer or sail (The pilot will *navigate* the plane with the help of maps and radar.)

propel   V. to cause to move forward (The powerful jet engines *propel* the plane down the runway.)

queasy   ADJ. nauseated (The motion of the plane made the man feel so *queasy* that he could not eat his meal.)

retractable   ADJ. able to be drawn in (The landing gear on an airplane is *retractable* so the wheels are pulled up into the plane after take-off.)

serene   ADJ. calm; peaceful (A glider ride is *serene* because the flight is smooth and there is no engine noise.)

simulate   V. to act like; to imitate (A disaster team will often *simulate* an airport accident in order to practice for the real thing.)

squadron   N. a group of eight or more airplanes that fly together (The planes in the World War II fighter *squadron* took off at the same time.)

taxi   V. to move slowly along the ground (After landing, an airplane will *taxi* from the runway to the landing gate.)

terminal   N. the building at the point where planes arrive and depart (When the airplane landed, the passengers rushed to the *terminal* to pick up their luggage and go home.)

turbulent   ADJ. stormy and unsettled (*Turbulent* weather caused the airplane to rock from side to side.)

Exercise 1
Write the letter of the word that best completes the sentence.

1. As the inspector walked among the planes in the _____, he checked to see if repairs were completed.
   A. cargo   B. cockpit   C. hangar   D. altitude   _____

2. Airplanes will slowly _____ to the edge of the runway and wait for instructions from the control tower.
   A. taxi   B. decrease   C. descend   D. simulate   _____

3. The young pilot sat nervously in the _____ as she prepared for her first solo flight.   _____
   A. aviation   B. altitude   C. cargo   D. cockpit

4. The children were excited as they watched their mother's plane _____ from the   _____
   sky and land on the runway.
   A. taxi   B. descend   C. decrease   D. simulate

5. The plane flew at a higher _____ to avoid the storm below.   _____
   A. terminal   B. squadron   C. hangar   D. altitude

6. The man's private jet was not working properly, so he flew on a _____ airline.   _____
   A. turbulent   B. abrupt   C. commercial   D. serene

7. You could only see the roof of the house from the _____ photograph.   _____
   A. commercial   B. queasy   C. aerial   D. retractable

8. Upon command the _____ of planes took off, one after the other in a straight line.   _____
   A. terminal   B. squadron   C. cargo   D. altitude

9. Because of poor _____, the airplane kept breaking down.   _____ ___
   A. cargo   B. altitude   C. maintenance D. terminal

10. The pilot pushed a button to lower the _____ radio antennae.   _____
    A. serene   B. queasy   C. abrupt   D. retractable

Exercise 2

Write the letter of the word that most nearly has the *same* meaning as the italicized
word.

11. *navigate*	A. slide	B. empty	C. guide	D. play	_____
12. *turbulent*	A. rough	B. slight	C. wise	D. shiny	_____
13. *decrease*	A. report	B. lessen	C. find	D. allow	_____
14. *abrupt*	A. empty	B. soft	C. loud	D. unexpected	_____
15. *cargo*	A. load	B. engine	C. book	D. wheel	_____
16. *queasy*	A. quiet	B. confused	C. sick	D. tired	_____
17. *simulate*	A. fake	B. brake	C. pour	D. speed	_____
18. *serene*	A. afraid	B. calm	C. nervous	D. mad	_____
19. *terminal*	A. station	B. motel	C. middle	D. fire	_____
20. *altitude*	A. bottom	B. concrete	C. height	D. tower	_____

Lesson 15
Health and Medicine

All the words in this lesson may be associated with health and medicine.

abnormal ADJ. not as it should be; not ordinary (The patient's *abnormal* heartbeat was faster than usual.)

addictive ADJ. habit-forming (If she continues to take too much medicine that is *addictive*, she will begin to need the medicine even when she is no longer ill.)

antibiotic N. a substance that will weaken germs and kill infection (The doctor said the *antibiotic* would cure the child's ear infection.)

antidote N. a medicine or substance that fights a poison (The Poison Control Center will tell you which *antidote* to give to someone who has accidentally swallowed a poison.)

consciousness N. the state of being aware of one's surroundings (He could not remember the ride to the hospital because he had lost *consciousness* in the ambulance.)

contagious ADJ. spread by contact (Because flu is a *contagious* disease, you may become ill if you are near someone who has the flu.)

contaminate V. to make impure (Untreated sewage can *contaminate* drinking water and cause people to become ill.)

convalesce V. to regain health after an illness (The patient was told to stay in bed and *convalesce* after her operation.)

diagnose V. to identify an illness or disease by examining (After seeing the boy's red spots, the doctor was able to *diagnose* the disease as chicken pox.)

disable V. to weaken or take away ability (A broken arm will *disable* a swimmer for at least six weeks.)

fracture N. a breaking of a bone (The doctor knew the girl had a *fracture* because the x-ray showed a crack in the bone.)

injection N. the act of forcing a liquid through the skin into a blood vein or a muscle (The nurse used a needle for the *injection* of allergy medicine into the boy's arm.)

irritate V. to rub or make red and sore (Too much sun causes sunburn which will *irritate* your skin.)

nauseous ADJ. causing a sick feeling in the stomach (Because the girl felt *nauseous*, the thought of food made her feel sick.)

sterilize V. to make free from germs (Using boiling water to *sterilize* medical instruments will kill most germs.)

surgeon N. a doctor who performs operations (The *surgeon* removed the boy's appendix.)

symptom N. a sign or change that indicates an illness or disease (Sneezing is one *symptom* of a cold.)

therapy N. treatment to help recover from a disease or disorder (Lifting weights was part of the boy's *therapy* to rebuild the muscles in his injured arm.)

vaccinate V. to inject with disease germs as a protection against a disease (A small amount of polio virus is given to children to *vaccinate* them against polio.)

vital ADJ. needed for life (When a *vital* organ such as the heart stops working, a person is close to death.)

Exercise 1
Write the letter of the word that best completes the sentence.

1. When you have a _____ disease, it is important to stay away from others. _____
   A. vital   B. contagious   C. addictive   D. nauseous

2. The bone _____ in her right arm took eight weeks to heal. _____
   A. fracture   B. surgeon   C. symptom   D. antidote

3. The nicotine in cigarettes is _____, making it difficult to stop smoking. _____
   A. abnormal   B. vital   C. nauseous   D. addictive

4. After suffering from a stroke which affected his speech, the man received _____ _____
   to help him learn to speak again.
   A. therapy   B. consciousness   C. antidote   D. surgeon

5. Hospitals must _____ all equipment and clothing used in an operating room. _____
   A. vaccinate   B. disable   C. sterilize   D. irritate

6. Penicillin is a(n) _____ that will stop infections. _____
   A. symptom   B. fracture   C. consciousness   D. antibiotic

7. A veterinarian will _____ pets against rabies so they will not get the deadly _____
   disease.
   A. convalesce   B. vaccinate   C. irritate   D. sterilize

8. While hiking in the desert, you should take along a(n)_____ for poisonous snake _____
   bites.
   A. therapy   B. symptom   C. antidote   D. fracture

9. The doctor felt that the kidney transplant was _____ to save the woman's life. _____
   A. vital   B. contagious   C. addictive   D. abnormal

10. The _____ performed the delicate operation and saved the girl's life. _____
    A. injection   B. antidote   C. surgeon   D. fracture

Exercise 2

Write the letter of the word that most nearly has the *same* meaning as the italicized word.

11. *injection*	A. pill	B. instrument	C. shot	D. clamp	_____
12. *contaminate*	A. tease	B. clean	C. invite	D. pollute	_____
13. *abnormal*	A. bright	B. neat	C. unusual	D. complex	_____
14. *disable*	A. cripple	B. delay	C. use	D. cure	_____
15. *irritate*	A. wash	B. inflame	C. start	D. empty	_____
16. *consciousness*	A. sleep	B. present	C. career	D. awareness	_____
17. *convalesce*	A. recover	B. resign	C. operate	D. walk	_____
18. *nauseous*	A. happy	B. confused	C. well	D. ill	_____
19. *symptom*	A. figure	B. time	C. sign	D. sound	_____
20. *diagnose*	A. talk	B. name	C. pay	D. wonder	_____

Lesson 16
Plants

All the words in this lesson may be associated with plants.

abundant   ADJ. more than enough (The *abundant* rainfall had filled the rivers to overflowing.)

alpine   ADJ. of mountains (Small *alpine* plants grow close together so they can survive the cold mountain climate.)

annual   ADJ. plants living only one season (Because beans and carrots are *annual* plants, farmers must replant them each year.)

botanist   N. a person who studies plants and plant life (The *botanist* used a microscope to examine the leaf's cell structure.)

conifer   N. a tree or shrub that bears cones (The giant sequoia of California is a *conifer* with enormous pine cones.)

convert   V. to change; to turn into another (Plants *convert* energy from sunlight into starch that can be used for food.)

deter   V. to keep back, hinder (Sharp thorns will *deter* an animal from eating a rose bush.)

dormant   ADJ. without activity (Grass looks dead in winter, but it is only *dormant* and will turn green in the spring.)

eradicate   V. to get rid of; to destroy (The gardener used weedkiller on the lawn to *eradicate* bothersome weeds.)

germinate   V. to sprout (If the seed does not *germinate,* the plant will not grow.)

medicinal   ADJ. useful as medicine; helpful (Ginsing is a *medicinal* plant that some people take to recover from illness.)

nursery   N. a place where plants and trees are raised for sale (We went to the *nursery* to buy new shrubs and vegetable plants.)

pollinate   V. to spread pollen for fertilization (Bees *pollinate* flowers by carrying tiny pollen grains from one plant to another.)

scatter   V. to throw around; to sprinkle (When the wind blows, it will *scatter* the small grass seeds over the ground.)

seedling   N. a young tree (The small *seedling* grew into a giant oak tree.)

spiral   ADJ. winding (The bean plant wound around the pole in a *spiral* formation.)

succulent   ADJ. juicy (Juice dripped down his chin as he bit into the *succulent* peach.)

symmetrical   ADJ. having exact agreement in size and shape; a mirror image (If you cut a daisy in half, you will see that it is *symmetrical* because both sides will look the same.)

tendril   N. a thin feeler that attaches itself to something for support (The morning glory's *tendril* curled around the fence post.)

thrive   V. to grow strong (Most plants will not *thrive* without sunshine and water.)

Exercise 1
Write the letter of the word that best completes the sentence.

1. The _____ examined forest plants before she wrote a book on wildflowers.   _____
   A. conifer   B. seedling   C. nursery   D. botanist

2. Seeds will often grow faster is they are allowed to _____ inside before being   _____
   planted outdoors.
   A. eradicate   B. germinate   C. convert   D. deter

3. Flowers depend on bees and butterflies to _____ them by carrying their pollen   _____
   from flower to flower.
   A. eradicate   B. convert   C. pollinate   D. scatter

4. The children gathered pine cones under the tall _____ in the woods.   _____
   A. conifer   B. tendril   C. botanist   D. seedling

5. The _____ sold many varieties of fruit trees.   _____
   A. tendril   B. seedling   C. conifer   D. nursery

6. At high altitudes, you can find _____ flowers growing in rocky places.   _____
   A. dormant   B. alpine   C. annual   D. spiral

7. Plants are able to _____ sunlight into food.   _____
   A. thrive   B. germinate   C. convert   D. scatter

8. The tiny _____ was shaded by large trees and did not grow well.   _____
   A. nursery   B. seedling   C. botanist   D. tendril

9. Every year Mark plants _____ flowers in the garden.   _____
   A. alpine   B. medicinal   C. annual   D. dormant

10. The plant's _____ reached out and attached itself to the tree trunk.   _____
    A. tendril   B. conifer   C. seedling   D. botanist

Exercise 2

Write the letter of the word that most nearly has the *opposite* meaning of the italicized word.

11. *symmetrical*	A. unbalanced	B. thin	C. alone	D. slow	_____
12. *thrive*	A. buy	B. listen	C. insist	D. die	_____
13. *abundant*	A. scarce	B. difficult	C. hungry	D. several	_____
14. *deter*	A. store	B. play	C. encourage	D. change	_____
15. *medicinal*	A. bright	B. harmful	C. quick	D. heavy	_____
16. *succulent*	A. dry	B. sweet	C. bitter	D. deep	_____
17. *scatter*	A. study	B. dig	C. gather	D. rid	_____
18. *eradicate*	A. build	B. erase	C. arrange	D. rid	_____
19. *spiral*	A. worn	B. dark	C. straight	D. fresh	_____
20. *dormant*	A. active	B. cold	C. quiet	D. strong	_____

Lesson 17
The Zoo

All the words in this lesson may be associated with zoos.

artificial   ADJ. not natural; made by humans rather than nature (In a zoo, air conditioning is used to keep penguins in an *artificial* climate that is always cold and wet.)

aviary   N. a large cage or house in which birds are kept (The fine net that covered many trees created a large *aviary* for the birds.)

barrier   N. an obstacle; something that prevents escape (A ditch is often used as a natural *barrier* to keep elephants and lions at a safe distance from zoo visitors.)

breed   V. to cause to produce young; to raise (Many zoos *breed* animals to increase the number of certain rare types.)

captivity   N. being held against one's will (Animals in *captivity* are usually put inside a fence or cage.)

contain   V. to hold back or restrain (Some zoos have large cages to *contain* the animals.)

curator   N. the person in charge of a zoo, museum, or library (The zoo's *curator* decided to purchase the pair of rare parrots.)

diverse   ADJ. different; various (There were many kinds of animals in the zoo's *diverse* collection.)

domestic   ADJ. tame (The wildlife exhibit does not include horses, cows, and pigs because they are *domestic* animals.)

eliminate   V. to get rid of (Zoo doctors are developing vaccines that will *eliminate* some animal diseases.)

exotic   ADJ. not native; foreign (The New Yorkers were amazed by the zoo's *exotic* birds from South America.)

habitat   N. the place where an animal lives (The natural *habitat* of the zebra is a dry grassy plain.)

preservation   N. keeping safe (Because the zoo is concerned with animal *preservation* it gives visitors information about animals whose natural homes are being destroyed.)

quarantine   V. to isolate from others to prevent the spread of disease (Doctors must *quarantine* new animals in a separate area of the zoo until they are checked for disease.)

reject   V. to refuse to accept (Sometimes a zoo animal will *reject* its newborn baby and pay no attention to it.)

replicate   V. to copy or imitate (The zoo tried to *replicate* the monkey's environment by making his cage look just like the jungle.)

species   N. a group of animals that are related (A tiger belongs to the cat *species*.)

tropical   ADJ. of the tropics or warm parts of the earth (The *tropical* fish were brought from the Pacific Islands near the equator.)

vicious   ADJ. savage, fierce (A mother animal may become *vicious* and attack someone who comes near her young.)

zoology   N. the study of animals (The professor of *zoology* gave a lecture on the habits of baboons.)

Exercise 1
Write the letter of the word that best completes the sentence.

1. The _____ birds were kept in an area that was hot and humid.
   A. vicious   B. tropical   C. artificial   D. domestic   _____

2. A glass _____ allowed the children to get close to the snakes without touching them.   _____

   A. barrier   B. curator   C. zoology   D. species

3. The veterinarian had to _____ the sick llama to prevent other animals from becoming ill.   _____

   A. breed   B. replicate   C. reject   D. quarantine

4. The town's citizens were delighted when the _____ announced that the zoo had purchased two new elephants.   _____

   A. habitat   B. captivity   C. curator   D. species

5. The zoo's architects tried to _____ the high peaks of mountain goats natural habitat.   _____

   A. contain   B. breed   C. quarantine   D. replicate

6. John took a course in _____ because he was interested in animals.   _____

   A. zoology   B. preservation   C. aviary   D. captivity

7. While walking through the _____, we enjoyed listening to the singing birds.   _____

   A. barrier   B. curator   C. aviary   D. captivity

8. The cement floors and cold steel bars in the lion's cage were quite unlike the lion's natural _____.   _____

   A. aviary   B. habitat   C. species   D. zoology

9. The zoo doctors will try to _____ the male and female panda bears in hopes of producing a new baby.   _____

   A. eliminate   B. contain   C. reject   D. breed

10. Zoos help protect endangered _____ by keeping them safe from natural enemies.   _____

   A. species   B. captivity   C. habitat   D. barrier

Exercise 2

Write the letter of the word that most nearly has the *opposite* meaning of the italicized word.

11. *artificial*	A. intense	B. solid	C. real	D. warm	_____
12. *exotic*	A. slow	B. cheap	C. careful	D. common	_____
13. *eliminate*	A. add	B. ring	C. attach	D. tie	_____
14. *diverse*	A. similar	B. sharp	C. unusual	D. warm	_____
15. *contain*	A. read	B. release	C. send	D. shout	_____
16. *captivity*	A. building	B. rainfall	C. ruin	D. freedom	_____
17. *reject*	A. accept	B. listen	C. unite	D. form	_____
18. *vicious*	A. careful	B. friendly	C. special	D. slow	_____
19. *domestic*	A. fat	B. bare	C. soft	D. wild	_____
20. *preservation*	A. destruction	B. animals	C. corner	D. grounds	_____

Lesson 18
Weather

All the words in this lesson may be associated with the weather.

barometer   N. an instrument that measures atmospheric pressure (Stormy weather is likely when the indicator on the *barometer* goes down.)

condense   V. to form drops as cooling occurs (As night comes, moisture in the air will *condense* into dew.)

cyclic   ADJ. relating to events that repeat themselves in recognizable patterns (The seasons are *cyclic* because they follow the same order year after year.)

devastate   V. to destroy completely (The powerful hurricane may *devastate* poorly built houses on the island.)

forecast   V. to know in advance (Listen to the weatherman *forecast* tomorrow's weather to learn whether you should plan a picnic.)

monsoon   N. the seasonal wind that brings heavy rains in India and southern Asia (People in Thailand prepared for flooding as the time of the *monsoon* grew near.)

observe   V. to examine scientifically (When the scientists *observe* sunspots, they will record changes that occur.)

ominous   ADJ. foretelling unfortunate events or weather (The *ominous* black clouds on the horizon warned us that a storm was coming.)

oppressive   ADJ. causing discomfort by being extreme (The *oppressive* weather was too hot for any energetic activity.)

perspiration   N. moisture excreted through the skin (As *perspiration* evaporates, it cools the body.)

prevailing   ADJ. predominant; usual (In the United States, the wind is usually from the west because the *prevailing* winds blow from west to east.)

rotation   N. turning around a fixed point (The *rotation* of the earth on its axis creates day and night.)

smog   N. a type of air pollution produced from smoke and fog (Although it was a clear day, thick *smog* made the air seem hazy.)

stratosphere   N. the upper layer of the earth's atmosphere (In the *stratosphere* there is less oxygen than in the air nearer the earth's surface.)

strike   V. to arrive violently (The blizzard will probably *strike* the city by late afternoon.)

swelter   V. to suffer from intense heat (Unless the air conditioning is repaired, we will *swelter* again tomorrow.)

swollen   ADJ. enlarged by excessive rainwater (After five days of rain, the *swollen* river washed away bridges.)

temperate   ADJ. characterized by mild weather with little temperature variation (People who dislike extremely cold or hot weather should live in a *temperate* climate.)

turbulence   N. violent, disorganized motion in the atmosphere or a fluid (The *turbulence* in the air blew the weather balloon from side to side.)

typhoon   N. a tropical storm in the western Pacific (The driving rain and high wind of the *typhoon* caused much damage in Japan.)

Exercise 1
Write the letter of the word that best completes the sentence.

1. The _____ of the weather vane indicates the direction of the wind.   _____
    A. monsoon   B. rotation   C. smog   D. stratosphere

2. If you hold a plate over a pan of boiling water, steam will _____ on it.   _____
    A. observe   B. strike   C. forecast   D. condense

3. It turned out to be a bad day for a hike because of the _____ heat and humidity.   _____
   A. swollen   B. cyclic   C. oppressive   D. temperate

4. Today should be fair since the reading on the _____ shows that the atmospheric   _____
   pressure has risen.
   A. turbulence   B. barometer   C. perspiration   D. monsoon

5. The police sound warning sirens when there is a chance that a tornado will _____   _____
   the village.
   A. strike   B. swelter   C. observe   D. condense

6. Because autumn is his favorite season, Rolf is glad that he lives in a(n) _____   _____
   climate.
   A. ominous   B. swollen   C. temperate   D. oppressive

7. During the season of the _____, it rains nearly every day in India.   _____
   A. barometer   B. turbulence   C. rotation   D. monsoon

8. As it rises through the _____, the weather balloon will relay information back to   _____
   scientists.
   A. perspiration   B. stratosphere   C. rotation   D. barometer

9. The exhaust from cars and buses creates _____ in large cities.   _____
   A. smog   B. monsoon   C. rotation   D. stratosphere

10. The trees tossed violently in the _____ of the windstorm.   _____
    A. smog   B. perspiration   C. barometer   D. turbulence

Exercise 2

Write the letter of the word that most nearly has the *same* meaning as the italicized word.

11. *swelter*   A. race   B. swim   C. steam   D. watch   _____
12. *typhoon*   A. millionaire B. fruit   C. monkey   D. hurricane   _____
13. *perspiration* A. sweat   B. disease   C. talent   D. flower   _____
14. *ominous*   A. wild   B. bright   C. threatening   D. huge   _____
15. *devastate*   A. travel   B. wreck   C. teach   D. feed   _____
16. *swollen*   A. red   B. hot   C. misty   D. overfilled   _____
17. *cyclic*   A. dense   B. rapid   C. repeating   D. correct   _____
18. *forecast*   A. predict   B. change   C. scare   D. repeat   _____
19. *prevailing*   A. noisy   B. common   C. interesting   D. dark   _____
20. *observe*   A. study   B. produce   C. entertain   D. convince   _____

Lesson 19
The Sea

All the words in this lesson may be associated with the sea.

afloat   ADJ. able to stay up in the water; not sinking (The ship remained *afloat* in spite of the terrible storm.)

breakwater   N. a wall or barrier that breaks the force of waves to protect a harbor or beach (Swimming was not allowed beyond the *breakwater* because of the strong currents.)

coastline   N. the outline of the land where it meets the sea (The Pilgrims sailed along the *coastline* of Massachusetts, looking for a good place to drop anchor.)

frigate   N. a fast naval vessel (A present-day *frigate* is often armed with guided missiles.)

gulf   N. a portion of the sea partly surrounded by land (Because it is protected, a *gulf* is often rich in sea life.)

heron   N. a long-legged water bird (We saw a beautiful *heron* wade through the shallow water of the bay.)

herring   N. a saltwater fish used for food (You can buy smoked *herring* in cans.)

hoist   V. to raise or lift (The sailors pulled up the sail when the captain gave orders to *hoist* the mainsail.)

keel   N. a piece running lengthwise under the center of a boat to keep it from blowing sideways (In the shallow water, the *keel* scraped against rocks and sand on the ocean floor.)

lofty   ADJ. very high (We saw the *lofty* sails on the tall masts of the Yankee Clipper ships.)

mariner   N. a sailor, especially one who helps navigate the ship (We will need an experienced *mariner* to guide the ship past the rocks.)

mutinous   ADJ. rebelling against the captain of a ship (When the crew became *mutinous* they refused to obey the captain's orders.)

oceanographer   N. a scientist who studies the physical characteristics of the ocean (The *oceanographer* helped prepare a map of the ocean.)

offshore   ADJ. away from the shore in a body of water (The oil company's rig for *offshore* drilling was stationed about two miles from the coast.)

relentless   ADJ. harsh or severe without relief (The *relentless* waves battered the tiny boat all day long.)

seafaring   ADJ. traveling or doing business by sea (The sailor preferred a *seafaring* life to one on land.)

submarine   N. a boat specially constructed to travel underwater (The *submarine* traveled below the surface of the water for several days.)

tidal   ADJ. relating to the rhythmic rise and fall of the waters of the ocean (The water in the *tidal* pools at the beach comes from sea water that has covered the rocks at high tide.)

vast   ADJ. of very great size or area (About seven-tenths of the earth's surface is covered by its *vast* oceans.)

yacht   N. any ship used for pleasure rather than business (On the banker's *yacht* there was a dining room and dance floor.)

Exercise 1
Write the letter of the word that best completes the sentence.

1. At certain times of the day, the seaweed that grows in the _____ waters is visible,   _____
but at other times it is deep underwater and cannot be seen.
   A. mutinous   B. tidal   C. relentless   D. seafaring

2. Sea gulls enjoy perching on the _____ that extends out into the harbor.   _____
   A. breakwater   B. oceanographer   C. keel   D. mariner

3. A life jacket will help you stay _____ if you are a weak swimmer.   _____
   A. lofty   B. vast   C. tidal   D. afloat

4. Laws forbid building too near the _____ to protect the view of the sea.   _____
   A. yacht   B. coastline   C. herring   D. frigate

5. The fishermen laid out their nets in hopes of getting a good catch of _____.   _____
   A. submarine   B. breakwater   C. herring   D. gulf

6. The children liked to swim to the _____ raft so they could practice diving in deep   _____
   water.
   A. afloat   B. tidal   C. mutinous   D. offshore

7. As the ship sailed into the _____, the winds were less intense than on the open   _____
   sea.
   A. gulf   B. submarine   C. heron   D. keel

8. After losing its _____, the boat leaned dangerously to one side.   _____
   A. breakwater   B. keel   C. yacht   D. coastline

9. The _____ will give a lecture about whether the oceans are warming because of   _____
   the greenhouse effect.
   A. frigate   B. oceanographer   C. coastline   D. keel

10. A periscope is used to look out of a _____ without bringing the ship to the surface   _____
    of the water.
    A. yacht   B. heron   C. mariner   D. submarine

Exercise 2

Write the letter of the word that most nearly has the *same* meaning as the italicized
word.

11. **mutinous**	A. helpful	B. defiant	C. sticky	D. noisy	_____
12. **heron**	A. nobleman	B. race car	C. bird	D. wig	_____
13. **mariner**	A. seaman	B. actor	C. driver	D. governor	_____
14. **relentless**	A. gloomy	B. heavy	C. calm	D. unceasing	_____
15. **frigate**	A. demon	B. book	C. ship	D. badge	_____
16. **seafaring**	A. landlocked	B. oceangoing	C. distant	D. underwater	_____
17. **yacht**	A. boat	B. sail	C. rope	D. underwater	_____
18. **hoist**	A. yell	B. point	C. lift	D. gaze	_____
19. **vast**	A. small	B. smooth	C. dry	D. huge	_____
20. **lofty**	A. tall	B. salty	C. short	D. windy	_____

Lesson 20
Travel

All the words in this lesson may be associated with travel.

accommodation   N. lodging; a place to stay (Our *accommodation* for the night was a little country inn.)

amusement   N. entertainment (In many small villages, the only *amusement* is the local movie theater.)

atlas   N. a book of maps (On every page of our road *atlas* there is a map of a different state.)

boulevard   N. a wide tree-lined street (The *boulevard* was lined with exclusive shops and giant elms.)

breakneck   ADJ. dangerously fast (To make the plane, the cab driver drove to the airport at *breakneck* speed.)

brochure   N. a leaflet or pamphlet (The travel agency gave us a four-page *brochure* with photographs of the resort.)

careen   V. to move with a rapid, uncontrolled motion (When the tire blew out, the car began to *careen* down the highway.)

convenient   ADJ. easy to get to (The swimming pool at the motel was *convenient* because it was just down the hall from our room.)

cram   V. to stuff (She hurriedly tried to *cram* her belongings into the small suitcase.)

depart   V. to leave (The train will *depart* from the station at 9:30.)

evacuate   V. to make empty (All the guests had to leave when there were orders to *evacuate* the hotel because of fire.)

fascinate   V. to create intense interest (The strange animals of Australia will *fascinate* the zoo director.)

itinerary   N. the plan of a journey (Our *itinerary* tells which cities we will visit each day next week.)

postpone   V. to put off (Because of the airline strike, we had to *postpone* our trip to Hawaii until next month.)

reliable   ADJ. that which can be trusted (The car proved to be *reliable,* for there were no breakdowns on the road.)

satchel   N. a small traveling bag (One change of clothing fit nicely into the *satchel* that she took on the overnight trip.)

skid   V. to slide (If you brake suddenly, the car will *skid* forward and make a screeching sound.)

strenuous   ADJ. needing much energy (They were exhausted after their *strenuous* climb up the mountain.)

traverse   V. to travel across (On the hike, it took us three days to *traverse* the wide mountain range.)

trek   N. a hard, slow, journey (The travelers were cold and weary after the long *trek* through the deep snow.)

Exercise 1
Write the letter of the word that best completes the sentence.

1. Before the trip we looked in the _____ for maps of the countries we should visit.   _____
   A. boulevard   B. amusement   C. atlas   D. satchel

2. The car began to _____ on the loose gravel of the mountain road.   _____
   A. traverse   B. fascinate   C. cram   D. skid

3. The airline announced it would _____ the plane because of a bomb threat.   _____
   A. evacuate   B. skid   C. traverse   D. depart

4. If you a looking for _____, you should go to the London Zoo.
   A. satchel   B. amusement   C. brochure   D. trek   _____

5. In the Amazon jungle we had to _____ a narrow rope bridge that stretched across   _____
a deep gorge.
   A. postpone   B. evacuate   C. traverse   D. trek

6. Marta checked the _____ to see when they were scheduled to arrive home.   _____
   A. brochure   B. satchel   C. atlas   D. itinerary

7. The tour guide tried to _____ too many people into the small bus.   _____
   A. cram   B. evacuate   C. depart   D. careen

8. At the airport we picked up a(n) _____ that listed the hotels in the city.   _____
   A. satchel   B. atlas   C. brochure   D. accommodation

9. We liked the _____ location of the hotel because it was a short walk to museums   _____
and shops.
   A. convenient   B. strenuous   C. breakneck   D. reliable

10. The runaway cart gathered speed as it began to _____ down the steep   _____
mountainside.
   A. cram   B. evacuate   C. traverse   D. careen

Exercise 2

Write the letter of the word that most nearly has the *same* meaning as the italicized
word.

11. **breakneck**	A. rapid	B. faint	C. single	D. far
12. **depart**	A. skip	B. speed	C. go	D. hang
13. **boulevard**	A. trail	B. avenue	C. park	D. arch
14. **reliable**	A. ordinary	B. sickly	C. heavy	D. dependable
15. **fascinate**	A. pull	B. amaze	C. count	D. translate
16. **satchel**	A. luggage	B. medicine	C. passport	D. book
17. **postpone**	A. hung	B. dig	C. delay	D. mail
18. **accommodation**	A. train	B. race	C. hotel	D. money
19. **strenuous**	A. easy	B. tiring	C. strong	D. comfortable
20. **trek**	A. parade	B. hike	C. race	D. music

Lesson 21
Time and Measurement

All the words in this lesson may be associated with elements of time and measurement.

abacus   N. beads in a frame used for doing arithmetic (Ancient Chinese mathematicians moved rows of beads on the *abacus* to make calculations.)

acute   ADJ. less than 90 degrees (A right triangle has two *acute* angles and one right angle.)

allow   V. to leave time or room for (If traffic is slow, you should *allow* more time than usual to get to the airport.)

comparative   ADJ. involving the descriptions of similarities or differences (A *comparative* measure of the two wires will tell which is longer.)

constant   N. a term in an equation that does not change its value (In the formula $A = \pi r^2$, the *constant* is π because it always equals the same thing.)

convert   V. to change from one unit of measure to another (If you *convert* temperature from Celsius to Fahrenheit, zero degrees will become thirty-two degrees.)

cubic   ADJ. of three dimensions (Volume is measured in *cubic* units because the measures of length, width, and height are involved.)

decimal   N. a fraction in which the denominator is 10 or a power of 10 and is shown with a point (We learned that 3/10 is a proper fraction, but .3 is a *decimal*.)

determine   V. to find out exactly (See if you can *determine* the length and width of the room with this tape measure.)

diagram   N. a drawing or plan to help explain something (The *diagram* of the engine helped me understand how a car works.)

expand   V. to spread out or enlarge (The area of a circle will increase if you *expand* the circumference.)

fathom   N. a unit of measure used at sea to measure the depth of water (One *fathom* is equal to six feet.)

geometric   ADJ. having to do with or composed of plane and solid figures (A series of triangles and hexagons created a *geometric* pattern on the Navajo rug.)

insoluble   ADJ. cannot be solved (No one in the class could find an answer to the *insoluble* problem.)

interim   N. the time in between (The mother was only gone a few minutes, but in the *interim*, the child was able to crawl out the door.)

intersect   V. to cross each other (Turn right at the corner where the north-south road and the east-west highway *intersect*.)

linear   ADJ. having only one dimension (Distance is *linear* measure because it concerns only length.)

logarithm   N. the exponent showing to what power a number must be raised to equal another number (The base ten *logarithm* of 100 is 2 because 10^2 is 100.)

protractor   N. a device for measuring and drawing angles (You should use a *protractor* to find the number of degrees in this angle.)

zigzag   N. a line with sharp turns back and forth (A *zigzag* looks like the letter z.)

Exercise 1
Write the letter of the word that best completes the sentence.

1. The five-gallon bucket held about 1200 _____ inches of water.   _____
   A. acute   B. geometric   C. cubic   D. comparative

2. Two lines _____ at one point.   _____
   A. allow   B. intersect   C. determine   D. convert

3. A variable in an equation can have different values, but the _____ has only one.   _____
   A. constant   B. diagram   C. protractor   D. abacus

4. Even though the problem seemed _____, he finally found an answer.   _____
   A. cubic   B. insoluble   C. geometric   D. linear

5. When buying food for the class party, you should _____ for extra guests.   _____
   A. intersect   B. allow   C. convert   D. determine

6. There were no curved lines in the _____ pattern.   _____
   A. cubic   B. comparative   C. insoluble   D. geometric

7. Our path was a _____ as we gradually climbed the mountain, crossing the   _____
   mountain face and then doubling back.
   A. decimal   B. fathom   C. interim   D. zigzag

8. I do not know how long the bus strike will last, but in the _____, we will have to   _____
   walk to school.
   A. logarithm   B. zigzag   C. interim   D. fathom

9. When you write $5.25, a _____ is used to show a quarter of a dollar.   _____
   A. logarithm   B. decimal   C. protractor   D. diagram

10. A ruler is used for _____ measure.   _____
    A. insoluble   B. acute   C. cubic   D. linear

11. Because they are exponents, you can add one _____ to another when you want   _____
    to multiply.
    A. zigzag   B. fathom   C. logarithm   D. interim

12. Half of a right angle is a(n) _____ angle.   _____
    A. acute   B. comparative   C. linear   D. cubic

13. To help decide which is better, we need a _____ study of the two plans.   _____
    A. geometric   B. cubic   C. comparative   D. linear

14. You multiply by twelve to _____ feet to inches.   _____
    A. allow   B. determine   C. intersect   D. convert

15. The clock was broken, so we could not _____ the correct time.   _____
    A. expand   B. determine   C. allow   D. convert

Exercise 2

Write the letter of the word pair that has a relationship similar to the relationship of the
first word pair.

16. **diagram : picture : :**   A. jar : container   C. sun : moon   _____
                                        B. drive : slowly   D. cup : saucer

17. **expand : contract : :**   A. song : music   C. full : empty   _____
                                        B. foot : shoe   D. stop : halt

18. **protractor : degrees : :**   A. hoe : gardener   C. work : play   _____
                                           B. feet : inches   D. scale : ounces

19. **abacus : calculator : :**   A. broom : vacuum   C. carry : load   _____
                                          B. cold : ice   D. hand : glove

20. **fathom : water : :**   A. inch : foot   C. ruler : scale   _____
                                     B. acre : land   D. soft : soften

Lesson 22
Verbal Communication

All the words in this lesson may be associated with verbal communication.

acclaim   V. to praise with enthusiasm (The class was eager to *acclaim* Josh as the winner of the debate.)

accolade   N. an honor or praise (John won an *accolade* from the principal for his effective leadership of the student council.)

acquaint   V. to make aware of; make known (Before the game, the referee will *acquaint* the players with the new rules.)

ambiguous   ADJ. having two or more possible meanings (The students' confusion was caused by the *ambiguous* instructions for the test.)

approval   N. a good opinion; consent (We have to get the teacher's *approval* for our topic before we begin writing the report.)

attitude   N. a feeling toward an issue or a person (Suzy expressed the *attitude* that the school should recycle its wastepaper.)

banter   N. light or playful remarks; teasing (Mike teases his sister with *banter* about her clothes and makeup.)

cajole   V. to persuade with flattery (By complimenting him on his good taste, Kyle tried to *cajole* his bother into letting him borrow the jacket.)

chastise   V. to criticize strongly (Mother looked stern as she began to *chastise* the girls for stepping on the newly planted flowers.)

confide   V. to discuss private matters or secrets (Although she would tell no one else about her plans to leave home, she decided to *confide* in her best friend.)

criticism   N. a discussion of strengths and weaknesses (In her *criticism* the reviewer praised the book for its vivid detail, but also commented on its poor plot line.)

defer   V. to yield to the opinion of someone else; to give in (Even though I would rather go to the movies, I will *defer* to your wish to rent a video.)

dialogue   N. conversation between two or more people (The two boys had a *dialogue* about the pros and cons of going out for basketball.)

embellish   V. to add made-up details (Kevin thought the simple truth would not convince his mother, so he decided to *embellish* his story with several events that never took place.)

enrage   V. to make very angry (Learning that all seats have been taken will *enrage* the man who has waited in line for two hours.)

fabricate   V. to make up; to invent (To explain why she was not at school, the girl will *fabricate* a story instead of telling the truth.)

flippant   ADJ. humorous in a slightly disrespectful way (Although a few people snickered at Laura's *flippant* remark to the teacher, most agreed that it was inappropriate and rude.)

harangue   N. an overly long, very passionate speech (After a while, we stopped listening to the gentleman's *harangue* about the selfishness of today's youth.)

refer   V. to send or direct someone to (I cannot answer your question, but I will *refer* you to someone who can.)

vehement   ADJ. showing strong feeling (He is *vehement* about closing down the city dump, and will not change his opinion.)

Exercise 1
Write the letter of the word that best completes the sentence.

1. Because he is unsure of himself, Brad finds it hard to accept _____.   _____
   A. criticism   B. approval   C. attitude   D. cajole

2. Please don't _____ an excuse for not doing your chores.
   A. fabricate   B. enrage   C. accolade   D. confide   _____

3. Since you are new in town, I will _____ you with some good restaurants.
   A. banter   B. confide   C. defer   D. acquaint   _____

4. As he told about his vacation, he decided to _____ the story to make it more
   interesting.
   A. harangue   B. enrage   C. embellish   D. refer   _____

5. If you want to hear about life in Australia, I'll _____ you to Juan, who visited there
   last summer.
   A. confide   B. defer   C. acclaim   D. refer   _____

6. His long _____ about the bad food in the cafeteria took most of the lunch hour.
   A. harangue   B. attitude   C. approval   D. dialogue   _____

7. If you _____ in me, I won't tell anyone.
   A. embellish   B. confide   C. acclaim   D. defer   _____

8. The audience laughed at the _____ between the two characters in the television
   show.
   A. accolade   B. approval   C. banter   D. vehement   _____

9. My father is _____ about people wearing seat belts, and will not start the
   engine until everyone is buckled in.
   A. flippant   B. ambiguous   C. acquaint   D. vehement   _____

10. His cheerful _____ makes him a pleasant co-worker.
    A. accolade   B. approval   C. attitude   D. criticism   _____

Exercise 2

Write the letter of the word that most nearly has the *opposite* meaning of the italicized
word.

11. *dialogue*   A. secret   B. food   C. monologue   D. book   _____

12. *defer*   A. point   B. ignore   C. fight   D. fill   _____

13. *approval*   A. form   B. sincerity   C. humor   D. rejection   _____

14. *flippant*   A. sincere   B. harmful   C. silent   D. alone   _____

15. *cajole*   A. smile   B. tear   C. follow   D. force   _____

16. *chastise*   A. inform   B. allow   C. praise   D. take   _____

17. *enrage*   A. part   B. soothe   C. engage   D. speak   _____

18. *ambiguous*   A. clear   B. shallow   C. crooked   D. distant   _____

19. *accolade*   A. drink   B. portion   C. necklace   D. disapproval   _____

20. *acclaim*   A. call   B. denounce   C. inform   D. sue   _____

Lesson 23
History

All the words in this lesson may be associated with historical events.

adversity   N. unfortunate events or conditions (The Pilgrims met with great *adversity* during the harsh winter in Plymouth.)

ally   N. a friendly nation, especially one involved in a shared goal (France was England's *ally* in World War I and the two countries fought on the same side again during World War II.)

annex   V. to take control of another country and make it part of one's own country (Texas became a state when the United States government decided to *annex* the Republic of Texas in 1845.)

aristocracy   N. a class of people who inherit titles or special privileges (Dukes, duchesses, counts and countesses were members of the *aristocracy* in France.)

avenge   V. to take revenge (From earliest times, people have tried to *avenge* a wrong by fighting.)

banish   V. to sentence someone to leave a place or country (When the king grew tired of a wife, he would *banish* her to a distant castle, and marry another woman.)

betray   V. to act to help an enemy of one's country (The agent persuaded the spy to *betray* his country and hand over the secret documents.)

brandish   V. to display in a threatening way (The general ordered the soldiers to *brandish* their swords in the air to intimidate the enemy.)

catapult   N. an ancient war machine that hurls large rocks or other objects (The soldier loosed the *catapult* and the burning torch was tossed inside the castle walls.)

coalition   N. a union formed to pursue a common goal (Several senators who usually disagree formed a *coalition* to pass the bill.)

conquest   N. a victory that leads to control over an enemy (Led by Hernando Cortes, the Spanish achieved a complete *conquest* over the Aztec Indians.)

document   V. to obtain or provide official evidence (Using the colonial woman's diary, the historian was able to *document* aspects of family life in the 1700's.)

emulate   V. to imitate successfully (Many countries would like to *emulate* the success of America's farming programs.)

feud   N. a long-standing disagreement (The *feud* between the two royal families had existed for over thirty years and was still causing bad feelings.)

genealogy   N. the study of family ancestries and histories (The *genealogy* of the boy's family showed that he was related to a king.)

ignorance   N. lack of knowledge or learning (The museum display helped us overcome our *ignorance* of how prehistoric man lived.)

immigrant   N. a person who comes to live in a new country (The *immigrant* from China was learning English so she could apply for citizenship in the United States.)

massacre   N. an unnecessary mass killing (Hundreds of women and children were killed in a senseless *massacre* by the invading army.)

recollect   V. to remember (His grandmother can *recollect* the time when school buses were horse-drawn wagons.)

seize   V. to take possession by force (The army will try to *seize* the capital by sneaking into the city under cover of night.)

Exercise 1
Write the letter of the word that best completes the sentence.

1. The queen will _____ the rebels and forbid them to reenter the country.   _____
   A. avenge   B. document   C. banish   D. feud

2. Prejudice is sometimes due to a(n) _____ of other cultures. _____
   A. ally   B. ignorance   C. immigrant   D. annex

3. Before 1914, Germany, Austria, and Turkey formed a _____ against France, _____
   Great Britain, Italy, and Russia.
   A. coalition   B. catapult   C. genealogy   D. conquest

4. The Indians attacked the settlement to _____ the death of their chief. _____
   A. emulate   B. avenge   C. feud   D. brandish

5. It is common for a(n) _____ to hope for a better life in his or her new country. _____
   A. annex   B. aristocracy   C. ignorance   D. immigrant

6. Before World War II, Germany decided to _____ Austria. _____
   A. annex   B. brandish   C. recollect   D. document

7. The people often suffer _____ when a country's resources are used to fight a war. _____
   A. aristocracy   B. immigrant   C. adversity   D. coalition

8. It is a serious crime to _____ government secrets to an enemy. _____
   A. brandish   B. betray   C. seize   D. recollect

9. Tax records are used by historians to _____ how people of the past lived. _____
   A. massacre   B. avenge   C. emulate   D. document

10. The common people rebelled against the _____ during the French Revolution. _____
    A. ally   B. ignorance   C. aristocracy   D. conquest

11. The king's forces avoided _____ by turning back the invading army. _____
    A. conquest   B. immigrant   C. genealogy   D. banishment

12. So many soldiers were killed, that the battle has been called a _____. _____
    A. feud   B. genealogy   C. catapult   D. massacre

13. The sailors boarded the ship to _____ the cargo. _____
    A. avenge   B. seize   C. betray   D. brandish

14. It was so long ago that he cannot _____ what happened. _____
    A. betray   B. avenge   C. recollect   D. annex

15. For years, the two cities had a _____ over which should be the state capital. _____
    A. feud   B. catapult   C. coalition   D. genealogy

Exercise 2

Write the letter of the word pair with a relationship similar to the relationship of the first word pair.

16. *ally : enemy : :*   A. ship : sea   C. factory : tank   _____
                              B. winner : loser   D. general : army

17. *brandish : sword : :*   A. grade : exam   C. wish : wealth   _____
                              B. hear : speech   D. wave : flag

18. *emulate : copy : :*   A. yell : sing   C. help : assist   _____
                              B. run : walk   D. hide : seek

19. *catapult : stone : :*   A. mask : face   C. war : peace   _____
                              B. truck : bus   D. gun : bullet

20. *genealogy : family : :* A. biography : person C. word : page   _____
                              B. author : book   D. map : globe

Lesson 24
Government

All the words in this lesson may be associated with government.

delegate   N. a person chosen to represent a group (Our homeroom chose Lee as its *delegate* to the student council.)

democratic   ADJ. governed by free elections (In a *democratic* country it is a right and a responsibility to vote.)

demonstrate   V. to make one's feelings about an issue known in an organized, public way (The students will *demonstrate* on Saturday in favor of the recycling law.)

diplomat   N. an official who lives in another country to represent his country's interests there (The Mexican *diplomat* discussed trade agreements with the President.)

disarm   V. to limit or get rid of military personnel or weapons (When the two countries *disarm,* the size of their armies will shrink.)

discord   N. disagreement (There is *discord* between the two countries because they cannot agree on how to fight air pollution.)

domestic   ADJ. having to do with a country's internal affairs (When the United States runs out of *domestic* oil, it will have to buy oil from another country.)

fanfare   N. a noisy display to attract attention (Speeches, free lemonade, and a brass band were part of the *fanfare* surrounding the candidate's visit.)

investigation   N. a detailed examination (Congress ordered an *investigation* of the senator's finances to see if campaign funds had been used improperly.)

levy   V. to require a tax or fee (The state will *levy* a deposit on all soft drink containers.)

liberal   N. having political views that favor progress and reform (The *liberal* representative from New York voted for the school tutoring program.)

neutral   ADJ. not taking either side (During the debate in Congress, the Senator remained *neutral* and refused to cast his vote for either side.)

parliament   N. the legislative body in some countries (Bills are voted into law during sessions of the *parliament* in Canada.)

slogan   N. a short, catchy phrase that conveys an important idea (During the Revolutionary War, the colonists chanted the *slogan,* "Don't tread on me.")

statesman   N. a person who shows great wisdom and skill in carrying out national affairs (Abraham Lincoln was a true *statesman* during the Civil War.)

stature   N. the position or rank achieved (The woman's high *stature* in government commanded the respect of all who knew her.)

staunch   ADJ. dedicated and steadfast (The *staunch* campaign worker never gave up trying, even when it looked as though the candidate would lose.)

suppress   V. to use power to stop actions or expression (The general wanted to *suppress* the newspapers so they could not print articles critical of his actions.)

tactic   N. a plan designed to help accomplish something (The candidate's *tactic* was to point out his opponent's faults.)

underdog   N. someone who is expected to lose in a contest (Although he was thought to be the *underdog,* Bill thinks he has a good chance of winning the election.)

Exercise 1
Write the letter of the word set that best completes the sentence.

1. The group will _____ in Washington to demand a(n) _____ of the incident.   _____
   A. suppress — delegate
   B. demonstrate — investigation
   C. disarm — fanfare
   D. levy — underdog

2. In the French embassy, the _____ met the _____ from the American trade union.   _____
   A. statesman — stature
   B. parliament — underdog
   C. diplomat — delegate
   D. fanfare — slogan

College of the Ouachitas

3. Because of his _____ as a _____, he was welcomed in every European country.   _____
   A. investigation — diplomat   C. slogan — delegate
   B. discord — underdog   D. stature — statesman

4. Every election day he worked hard to get voters to the polls because he was a   _____
   _____ believer in the _____ process.
   A. domestic — parliament   C. liberal — statesman
   B. staunch — democratic   D. neutral — diplomat

5. The dictator gave orders to _____ the revolutionary _____ that the group was chanting.   _____
   A. disarm — liberal   C. demonstrate — discord
   B. levy — tactic   D. suppress — slogan

6. A _____ member of the _____ sponsored the progressive bill.   _____
   A. liberal — parliament   C. staunch — tactic
   B. democratic — investigation   D. neutral — discord

7. Even though other countries were at war, Switzerland remained _____ and   _____
   refused to _____ taxes to build up its army.
   A. domestic — demonstrate   C. staunch — suppress
   B. democratic — disarm   D. neutral — levy

8. There was great _____ when the two countries announced plans to _____.   _____
   A. tactic — levy   C. discord — suppress
   B. fanfare — disarm   D. delegate — levy

9. If she uses a new _____, the _____ in the election might have a chance to win.   _____
   A. tactic — underdog   C. slogan — stature
   B. diplomat — fanfare   D. parliament — statesman

10. When there is _____ within a country, it is usually considered a _____ problem.   _____
    A. investigation — liberal   C. discord — domestic
    B. fanfare — staunch   D. parliament — neutral

Exercise 2

Write the letter of the word that most nearly has the *opposite* meaning to the italicized word.

11. *discord*	A. sadness	B. election	C. harmony	D. darkness	_____
12. *fanfare*	A. parade	B. calm	C. dinner	D. fantasy	_____
13. *disarm*	A. operate	B. cancel	C. choose	D. fortify	_____
14. *underdog*	A. cat	B. taker	C. favorite	D. lawyer	_____
15. *staunch*	A. unfaithful	B. stupid	C. kindly	D. short	_____
16. *neutral*	A. alone	B. biased	C. fast	D. content	_____
17. *suppress*	A. lose	B. try	C. entangle	D. encourage	_____
18. *domestic*	A. fuzzy	B. foreign	C. deep	D. weak	_____
19. *democratic*	A. together	B. happy	C. authoritarian	D. complex	_____
20. *liberal*	A. conservative	B. proud	C. important	D. elected	_____

Lesson 25
Agriculture

All the words in this lesson may be associated with agriculture.

acreage   N. number of acres (The *acreage* of his father's large farm was vast.)

arable   ADJ. fit for plowing (The sandy soil near the river is more *arable* than the rocky ground on a mountainside.)

disk   V. to work the soil with a disk plow (Before we plant the corn, we *disk* the field to soften the ground.)

fallow   ADJ. plowed and left unseeded (Smart farmers will leave a field *fallow* every five years to give the soil a rest.)

flax   N. a plant with stems that separate into threadlike parts that can be woven into linen (Early settlers made cloth from *flax* that they grew.)

harrow   N. a plow with iron teeth used to break up ground into fine pieces before planting seeds (Before planting the soybeans, drag the *harrow* across the field.)

harvest   V. to gather in grain or other food crops (The farmer will *harvest* the corn when the stalks and kernels have dried.)

horticulture   N. the science or art of growing plants and vegetables (When he studied *horticulture,* my brother learned about ways to prevent plant disease.)

husbandry   N. careful management of resources; conservation (The rancher's *husbandry* of the land resulted in a large crop on just a few acres.)

husk   N. the outer layer of many fruits and seeds (The process of threshing separates the *husk* from the wheat seed.)

hydroponics   N. the growing of plants without soil by using water that contains necessary nutrients (Juan believes that *hydroponics* will replace agriculture when land becomes scarce.)

industrious   ADJ. very hard-working (She is an *industrious* worker, for she rises early and starts the chores before daybreak.)

kernel   N. a grain or seed like that of wheat or corn (When we are down to our last *kernel* of corn, we will buy more.)

livestock   N. animals such as cattle, sheep, horses, or hogs that are raised for home use or profit (We buy grain for the *livestock* to eat during the winter.)

pesticide   N. a substance used to kill insects and rodents (Using a *pesticide* on crops may prevent insect damage, but it can also harm the environment.)

reap   V. to gather a crop by cutting (Swinging a tool with a sharp blade, the field hand began to *reap* the grain.)

rural   ADJ. in the country (Many people prefer *rural* living to city life because of the peace and quiet.)

rustic   ADJ. belonging to the country; plain, old-fashioned (The *rustic* farm did not even have indoor plumbing.)

seasonable   ADJ. suitable to the season (In the North, snow is *seasonable* in January.)

till   V. to plow (Long ago, farmers would *till* the fields with a horse-drawn plow.)

Exercise 1
Write the letter of the word set that best completes the sentence.

1. The farmer will _____ the asparagus in March because it is a _____ crop.   _____
   A. harvest — industrious   C. harvest — seasonable
   B. harvest — rustic   D. disk — rural

2. We bought some _____ in a(n) _____ area to have room for a large garden.   _____
   A. acreage — industrious   C. flax — rural
   B. flax — industrious   D. acreage — rural

3. The _____ on an ear of corn protects each _____.
   A. husk — kernel
   B. harrow — kernel
   C. kernel — husk
   D. pesticide — husk

4. Because of his lack of _____, the farmer must sell his _____.
   A. pesticide — acreage
   B. husbandry — livestock
   C. acreage — husbandry
   D. horticulture — husbandry

5. While studying _____ at the university, John took a course in _____ and learned to grow plants in water.
   A. livestock — hydroponics
   B. horticulture — hydroponics
   C. hydroponics — livestock
   D. horticulture — husbandry

6. The _____ land on Midwestern farms makes it possible to _____ good corn crops.
   A. fallow — till
   B. seasonal — reap
   C. fallow — disk
   D. arable — reap

7. Even though the farmer had planned to _____ the soil, he decided to leave the field _____ because there was no demand for soybeans.
   A. reap — fallow
   B. disk — rural
   C. disk — fallow
   D. disk — industrious

8. The _____ seemed out of place in the clean _____ environment.
   A. pesticide — rustic
   B. flax — seasonable
   C. flax — rustic
   D. pesticide — seasonable

9. The _____ field hand dragged a _____ behind the tractor to prepare the field.
   A. arable — harrow
   B. industrious — harrow
   C. industrious — kernel
   D. arable — kernel

10. After we _____ the soil, we will plant _____ and use it to make our own cloth.
    A. till — flax
    B. harvest — harrow
    C. till — harrow
    D. harvest — livestock

Exercise 2

Write the letter of the word that most nearly has the *same* meaning as the italicized word.

11. *industrious*   A. lazy   B. energetic   C. loud   D. cruel
12. *till*   A. run   B. empty   C. plow   D. sift
13. *arable*   A. fertile   B. rough   C. new   D. big
14. *livestock*   A. grain   B. animals   C. pen   D. snow
15. *fallow*   A. wet   B. last   C. high   D. barren
16. *rustic*   A. simple   B. modern   C. fancy   D. blue
17. *harvest*   A. clothe   B. gather   C. eat   D. help
18. *kernel*   A. plant   B. root   C. leaf   D. seed
19. *pesticide*   A. lotion   B. tail   C. poison   D. cart
20. *husk*   A. shell   B. quiet   C. spice   D. stem

Lesson 26
Law

All the words in this lesson may be associated with the field of law.

adversary   N. opponent; person or group on the other side in a contest (The public defender's chief *adversary* was the attorney for the prosecution.)

apparent   ADJ. plain to see (The evidence made it very *apparent* that the man had committed the crime.)

bailiff   N. the officer who guards prisoners while they are in a courtroom (The judge asked the *bailiff* to release the prisoner who had just been found not guilty.)

blackmail   V. to get money or favors from a person by threatening to tell something bad about him or her (Tim tried to *blackmail* John by saying he would tell John's mother about the lost jacket unless John helped him with his homework.)

clemency   N. mercy (Rather than execute the prisoners of war, the government showed *clemency* and released them.)

condemn   V. to pronounce guilty of a crime; to sentence or doom (The jury had no choice but to *condemn* the man to life in prison.)

conviction   N. the condition of being proved guilty (In most states, a second *conviction* for drunken driving will result in a jail term.)

deceive   V. to mislead (A guilty criminal may hope that lying will *deceive* the judge.)

defense   N. the side that speaks for the person who is accused of a crime (The *defense* had to call many witnesses to prove that the man on trial was not guilty.)

entrap   V. to trick (A skillful lawyer can *entrap* witnesses and get them to say things they weren't planning to admit.)

faulty   ADJ. having faults; defective (Because his argument was *faulty*, the lawyer lost the case.)

imprison   V. to put in prison; restrain (The sheriff's orders were to *imprison* anyone who drew a gun.)

involuntary   ADJ. not performed by one's own free choice (Because the man had not meant to knock down the policeman, he was charged with *involuntary* assault.)

manacle   N. an iron handcuff that will restrain a prisoner's hands and feet (A *manacle* chained the prisoner's leg to an iron post.)

motive   N. reason that makes a person act a certain way (The boy said that his *motive* for stealing the cookies was hunger.)

objective   ADJ. impersonal; giving facts as they are without favoring either side (A judge must remain completely *objective*, deciding each case on the basis of fact alone.)

parole   N. a conditional release from jail before the full sentence has been served (Because the convict was granted *parole*, he may leave the prison before finishing his sentence.)

reasonable   ADJ. fair; as dictated by common sense (To find a person guilty of a crime, the jury must be sure of his guilt beyond a *reasonable* doubt.)

relevant   ADJ. related; pertinent (Since the testimony had nothing to do with the events in the trial, the judge ruled that it was not *relevant* to the case.)

valid   ADJ. supported by facts or evidence; effective (If the lawyer's argument is not *valid*, the judge will reject it.)

Exercise 1
Write the letter of the word that best completes the sentence.

1. The prisoner was released on _____ after serving half his term.   _____
   A. parole   B. defense   C. motive   D. clemency

2. The detective tried to _____ the suspect by letting him think that he already knew who the robber was. _____

   A. imprison   B. condemn   C. entrap   D. blackmail

3. The prisoner was able to pull his hand out of the _____ and escape. _____

   A. bailiff   B. parole   C. manacle   D. conviction

4. The _____ escorted the prisoner back to his cell when the trial was over. _____

   A. adversary   B. clemency   C. parole   D. bailiff

5. Because there was not a _____ for the crime, the police were puzzled. _____

   A. motive   B. manacle   C. parole   D. bailiff

6. After the man was found guilty, many people expected the judge to _____ him to several years in prison. _____

   A. entrap   B. condemn   C. deceive   D. blackmail

7. The criminal tried to _____ the jury by acting as if he knew nothing of the crime. _____

   A. blackmail   B. condemn   C. deceive   D. imprison

8. The jury believed the _____ and allowed the accused woman to go free. _____

   A. clemency   B. bailiff   C. manacle   D. defense

9. The woman threatened to _____ her boss by telling the newspapers about his shady business deals. _____

   A. blackmail   B. condemn   C. imprison   D. entrap

10. The judge may _____ the witness if she does not answer his questions. _____

   A. blackmail   B. deceive   C. imprison   D. entrap

Exercise 2

Write the letter of the word that most nearly has the *opposite* meaning as the italicized word.

11. *objective*   A. fair   B. important   C. alike   D. biased   _____

12. *defense*   A. prosecution   B. work   C. nothing   D. mercy   _____

13. *faulty*   A. apart   B. broken   C. perfect   D. weak   _____

14. *reasonable*   A. tight   B. hard   C. delicate   D. ridiculous   _____

15. *adversary*   A. teammate   B. pilot   C. uncle   D. carpenter   _____

16. *valid*   A. kind   B. careful   C. ineffective   D. playful   _____

17. *apparent*   A. unclear   B. cruel   C. tremendous   D. handy   _____

18. *relevant*   A. good   B. undone   C. unrelated   D. final   _____

19. *involuntary*   A. payable   B. youthful   C. difficult   D. deliberate   _____

20. *conviction*   A. tale   B. acquittal   C. beginning   D. glass   _____

Lesson 27
Arts and Crafts

All the words in this lesson may be associated with arts and crafts.

aptitude   N. natural talent; ability (John can fix the chair because he has a great *aptitude* for woodworking.)

art   N. a specific skill or craft (Since he has been practicing the *art* of breadmaking for years, his rolls are excellent.)

ceramics   N. the art of making pottery (When I studied *ceramics,* I learned how to make my own cups and bowls out of clay.)

daub   V. to cover or smear; to paint coarsely (Maria will *daub* a few splotches of red paint on her picture to add color.)

discernible   ADJ. capable of being recognized or seen clearly (The image of the man's face was barely *discernible* in the faded watercolor.)

distraction   N. anything that draws attention away from what one is doing or thinking (The honking horn outside was a *distraction* to the potter.)

diversion   N. amusement; entertainment (Going to the art festival will be a pleasant *diversion* on a Saturday afternoon.)

engrave   V. to carve or cut figures in lines on a metal plate or block of wood (For a small fee, the jeweler will *engrave* your initials on the bracelet.)

finesse   N. skill; delicate or controlled execution (To carve the intricate design requires *finesse* with the knife.)

flamboyant   ADJ. showy; colorful (The *flamboyant* purple tie will attract attention.)

glossy   ADJ. smooth and shining (Kevin polished the *glossy* metal bowls until they shone like glass.)

gouge   V. dig out; force out (The woodcarver used a small knife to *gouge* a rough outline of the design for the wooden bowl.)

lacquer   N. varnish that gives a protective coating to wood and metal (A good coat of *lacquer* on the table top will keep the wood from getting stained.)

magenta   ADJ. purplish-red in color (The *magenta* bowl matched the plums on the table.)

malleable   ADJ. able to be shaped by pounding (Silver is so *malleable* that it can be hammered into any shape.)

mallet   N. a hammer with a barrel-shaped head (John used a rubber *mallet* to pound the table leg to avoid damaging the wood.)

mar   V. to damage or disfigure (Dropping the heavy iron may *mar* the floor's finish.)

outlet   N. a store that sells goods from a particular manufacturer or wholesaler (He buys his paints from an art supply *outlet* on the edge of town.)

pigment   N. a substance used as coloring (When she mixed the *pigment* into the white paint, it turned a lovely shade of blue.)

shatter   V. to break into pieces (If the glass bowl should *shatter,* there will be many glass slivers to sweep up.)

Exercise 1
Write the letter of the word set that best completes the sentence.

1. The pottery maker showed she was a master at _____ by demonstrating her _____ on the pottery wheel.   _____
   A. diversion — finesse   C. ceramics — finesse
   B. pigment — diversion   D. ceramics — pigment

2. The artist used a _____ to _____ the glass bottles.   _____
   A. mallet — shatter   C. mallet — daub
   B. lacquer — shatter   D. mallet — gouge

3. The cabinetmaker had to _____ wood filler over the nail holes before brushing on a coat of _____. _____
   A. mar — lacquer
   B. shatter — pigment
   C. daub — finesse
   D. daub — lacquer

4. The young girl's _____ for art was scarcely _____ because she had drawn very little. _____
   A. aptitude — flamboyant
   B. distraction — glossy
   C. distraction — discernible
   D. aptitude — discernible

5. The loud noise was a _____ that caused the sculptor to _____ the statue with his knife. _____
   A. mallet — gouge
   B. distraction — gouge
   C. distraction — shatter
   D. mallet — shatter

6. The Native American engaged in the _____ of pounding the _____ copper into fine jewelry. _____
   A. ceramics — malleable
   B. ceramics — discernable
   C. art — malleable
   D. diversion — discernible

7. Special care must be taken or sunlight will _____ the _____ photographs. _____
   A. mar — glossy
   B. shatter — discernible
   C. gouge — magenta
   D. engrave — flamboyant

8. The fabric supply _____ sells a special _____ that can be used to dye yarn. _____
   A. lacquer — pigment
   B. outlet — pigment
   C. pigment — outlet
   D. outlet — art

9. Instead of work, he considers it a _____ to _____ designs on silver bracelets. _____
   A. finesse — engrave
   B. distraction — mar
   C. diversion — engrave
   D. finesse — mar

10. The _____ painter attracted more attention with his _____ hat than with his art. _____
   A. flamboyant — magenta
   B. magenta — malleable
   C. discernible — finesse
   D. discernible — gorgeous

Exercise 2

Write the letter of the word that most nearly has the *opposite* meaning as the italicized word.

11. *diversion*	A. outing	B. task	C. meal	D. allowance	_____
12. *finesse*	A. kindness	B. problem	C. clumsiness	D. silence	_____
13. *glossy*	A. dull	B. colorful	C. beautiful	D. short	_____
14. *aptitude*	A. solution	B. inability	C. contest	D. fitness	_____
15. *discernible*	A. ample	B. close	C. foreign	D. hidden	_____
16. *malleable*	A. first	B. soft	C. hard	D. difficult	_____
17. *gouge*	A. fill	B. turn	C. paint	D. give	_____
18. *flamboyant*	A. airborne	B. round	C. big	D. plain	_____
19. *engrave*	A. open	B. question	C. erase	D. attempt	_____
20. *mar*	A. break	B. allow	C. repair	D. confuse	_____

Lesson 28
Art and Music

All the words in this lesson may be associated with fields of art and music.

alto   N. in singing, a low female voice (My older sister cannot reach the high notes, so she sings *alto* in the choir.)

angular   ADJ. lean, with outlines of bones visible (The ballerina, who weighed less than 100 pounds, had a thin, *angular* face.)

applaud   V. to praise and approve by clapping (If you like the music, please wait to *applaud* until the piece is completely finished.)

cancel   V. to nullify or cross out (Because of a nagging sore throat, the country singer was forced to *cancel* his concert.)

combo   N. a small group of musicians (The jazz *combo* consisted of a saxophonist, a guitar player, and a pianist.)

conduct   V. to direct or manage (When the orchestra leader raises her baton to *conduct,* the musicians get ready to play.)

gallery   N. a room or building used to display art works (The works of several young artists were hung in the *gallery*.)

harmonious   ADJ. arranged so all parts go well together (The *harmonious* sound of the children's choir filled the air.)

Illustrate   V. to provide pictures, maps, or diagrams that help clarify or ornament (The writer hired an artist to *illustrate* the children's story he had written.)

mural   N. a picture painted on a wall (When the office building was remodeled, the *mural* in the hallway was painted over.)

palette   N. a thin board on which painters mix their colors (Holding her *palette* in one hand, the artist blended red and yellow to make a light shade of orange.)

pastel   ADJ. soft and pale in color (The *pastel* pink in the painting was the color of a fresh peach.)

prior   ADV. preceding in time (The symphony rehearsed several times *prior* to the concert.)

quartet   N. a group of four singers or musicians performing together (There were three tenors and one bass singing in the barbershop *quartet.*)

radiant   ADJ. shining; beaming (The dancer's face was *radiant* as she received the bouquet of flowers.)

rave   V. to be wildly enthusiastic (When we heard the critics *rave* about the cast and the director, we knew the show was a hit.)

realism   N. in art, the picturing of life as it is (The painting was an example of *realism* because it showed the hard life of the Depression farmer.)

recital   N. a musical performance, usually given by a single performer (For her *recital,* the pianist played three pieces.)

sculptor   N. an artist who makes figures from blocks of stone, metal, or wood (A famous *sculptor* carved the marble statue at the entrance to the library.)

unique   ADJ. unusual; the only one of its kind (The guitar player's *unique* style was completely different from any we had heard.)

Exercise 1
Write the letter of the word that best completes the sentence.

1. Our musical _____ gets together once a week to play for school dances.   _____
   A. combo   B. gallery   C. palette   D. sculptor

2. The woman who painted the picture of the city slum belongs to the school of   _____

   _____.
   A. alto   B. gallery   C. realism   D. quartet

3. It took the _____ many years to carve the presidents' faces on Mount Rushmore.   _____
   A. quartet   B. combo   C. palette   D. sculptor

4. The choir needed a(n) _____ to sing the lower part of the song.   _____
   A. mural   B. alto   C. recital   D. realism

5. I hope the public will _____ when they see my newest painting.   _____
   A. rave   B. conduct   C. cancel   D. illustrate

6. The art students painted a _____ on the school wall showing important events in   _____
   their state's history.
   A. gallery   B. recital   C. mural   D. sculptor

7. The two voices blended sweetly as they sang the _____ melody.   _____
   A. harmonious   B. radiant   C. pastel   D. unique

8. The new _____opened with a showing of photographs from Ireland.   _____
   A. palette   B. mural   C. gallery   D. recital

9. A string _____ consists of two violins, a viola, and a cello.   _____
   A. quartet   B. gallery   C. sculptor   D. mural

10. At the end of the day, the artist scraped the paint off her _____ and put it away.   _____
    A. sculptor   B. mural   C. palette   D. alto

Exercise 2

Write the letter of the word that most early has the *same* meaning as the italicized
word.

11. *prior*	A. correct	B. low	C. dark	D. before	_____
12. *radiant*	A. round	B. calm	C. gleaming	D. dull	_____
13. *applaud*	A. add	B. start	C. help	D. clap	_____
14. *recital*	A. date	B. concert	C. skill	D. record	_____
15. *angular*	A. bony	B. petite	C. plump	D. huge	_____
16. *conduct*	A. allow	B. find	C. lead	D. give	_____
17. *cancel*	A. eliminate	B. allow	C. begin	D. suggest	_____
18. *illustrate*	A. reply	B. decorate	C. attempt	D. look	_____
19. *unique*	A. open	B. old	C. large	D. uncommon	_____
20. *pastel*	A. cold	B. light	C. dark	D. tall	_____

Lesson 29
Construction

All the words in this lesson may be associated with construction.

abode   N. a place to live in; a dwelling (Their simple *abode* was made from hand cut logs.)

abut   V. to be next to; to be up against (The house plans show that the house will *abut* the garage on one side.)

align   V. to arrange in a line (You must *align* the floor tiles so they are straight.)

assist   V. to help; give assistance (The carpentry students will *assist* the builder on the new construction project.)

bolster   V. to keep from falling down (Tom had to *bolster* up the collapsing shed with new beams.)

caulk   V. to fill in cracks to keep air or water from coming through (The carpenter used wood putty to *caulk* the holes around the windows.)

contractor   N. a person who will supply materials or services for a fee (The *contractor* handled all the plumbing and electrical work in the house.)

dwell   V. to live; to make one's home (They *dwell* in a farm house a few miles from the city.)

encase   V. to cover completely; to enclose (The electrician was careful to *encase* all the loose wires in a plastic covering.)

erect   V. to build (The city has plans to *erect* a new courthouse in the center of town.)

flaw   N. a defect (A *flaw* in the wiring caused the house fire.)

foundation   N. the part on which other parts rest (The concrete *foundation* formed a sturdy base for the house.)

hoist   V. to lift up (A crane was used to *hoist* the steel beams to the top of the building.)

install   V. to put in place for use (After breaking the window, the woman had to *install* a new one.)

insulate   V. to keep from losing heat, sound, or electricity (Because of the cold winters, people *insulate* their homes to keep the heat in.)

investment   N. something that is expected to yield money at a profit (Buying a home can be a good *investment* if the house is resold at a higher price.)

linoleum   N. a strong washable floor covering often used in kitchens (The builders put carpet in the living room and *linoleum* on the kitchen floor.)

mahogany   N. a hard, reddish-brown wood (The furniture maker used *mahogany* for the table and chairs.)

plywood   N. boards made by gluing several thin layers of wood together (*Plywood* is good for making bookshelves because it does not bend easily.)

privacy   N. the condition of being private (The family built a fence around their yard for *privacy*.)

Exercise 1
Write the letter of the word set that best completes the sentence.

1. The foreman used a forklift to _____ the cinder blocks onto the _____.   _____
   A. assist — plywood
   B. hoist — foundation
   C. encase — foundation
   D. insulate — linoleum

2. Before winter, you should _____ around your doors to help _____ your home.   _____
   A. hoist — insulate
   B. caulk — encase
   C. assist — insulate
   D. caulk — insulate

3. The _____ found a _____ in the roof that may have to be repaired. _____
   A. contractor — flaw   C. contractor — foundation
   B. plywood — mahogany   D. abode — foundation

4. Before he began to _____ the treehouse, Mark had to _____ up one weak limb _____
   of the tree with a long pole.
   A. abut — align   C. assist — abut
   B. bolster — caulk   D. erect — bolster

5. Because they _____ in a house surrounded by trees, they have plenty of _____. _____
   A. assist — privacy   C. assist — mahogany
   B. dwell — privacy   D. insulate — abode

6. The builder used _____ for the kitchen floor and _____ for the kitchen cabinets. _____
   A. linoleum — privacy   C. linoleum — mahogany
   B. mahogany — foundation   D. foundation — linoleum

7. To increase the value of his _____, Neal decided to _____ a swimming pool. _____
   A. flaw — install   C. privacy — install
   B. investment — install   D. investment — align

8. The walls of his summer _____ were made of _____. _____
   A. abode — plywood   C. investment — linoleum
   B. abode — privacy   D. foundation — plywood

9. The carpenter made sure to _____ the beams with the angle of the wall so the _____
   porch would evenly _____ the house.
   A. bolster — align   C. abut — insulate
   B. align — hoist   D. align — abut

10. John had to _____ the plumber as he worked to _____ the water pipes in _____
    insulation.
    A. dwell — encase   C. assist — erect
    B. assist — encase   D. install — hoist

Exercise 2

Write the letter of the word that most nearly has the *same* meaning as the italicized
word.

11. *encase*	A. lift	B. build	C. wrap	D. empty	_____
12. *abut*	A. touch	B. set	C. pry	D. glue	_____
13. *hoist*	A. mark	B. pretend	C. store	D. raise	_____
14. *align*	A. straighten	B. label	C. ring	D. hammer	_____
15. *caulk*	A. mix	B. burn	C. seal	D. dig	_____
16. *dwell*	A. sit	B. imagine	C. spin	D. reside	_____
17. *abode*	A. roof	B. trap	C. house	D. closet	_____
18. *flaw*	A. pen	B. fault	C. book	D. road	_____
19. *erect*	A. construct	B. create	C. destroy	D. knock	_____
20. *assist*	A. hinder	B. cut	C. pound	D. aid	_____

Lesson 30
Money and Finance

All the words in this lesson may be associated with money and finance.

acquire   V. to gain ownership or possession (The builder hopes to *acquire* the land so he can construct a new shopping center.)

affluent   ADJ. having a large amount of wealth or property (Many houses had swimming pools in the *affluent* neighborhood.)

boom   N. a period of rapid increase in price, numbers, or value (Many homes were built and sold during the *boom* in housing.)

cashier   N. a worker who totals up purchases and collects payment (After I paid the *cashier* at the grocery store, she gave me a receipt.)

clerical   ADJ. relating to general office work, such as typing and filing (LaTonya organized the company's files when she was a *clerical* worker last summer.)

customer   N. a person who buys goods or services (You will often see Bill in that store purchasing items because he is a loyal *customer*.)

depository   N. a place where money may be left safely (After the bank closes, you can put money through the slot of the *depository* and the bank will collect it in the morning.)

discount   N. a reduction in the usual price (Everything in the store will be sold at a *discount* during the sale.)

donate   V. to give (We *donate* some money to the fund for the homeless every year.)

hock   V. to leave something as security when borrowing money (The musician was forced to *hock* his keyboard to get money to pay the rent.)

insatiable   ADJ. not able to be fulfilled (Although he was a millionaire, his *insatiable* greed made him want more money.)

interest   N. a sum paid for the use of money (The bank will pay *interest* on money left in a savings account.)

invest   V. to put money to work in a way expected to make a profit (If you *invest* in the restaurant now, you can share in the profits later on.)

lucrative   ADJ. making a profit (Many people bought our lemonade at the soccer game, so it turned out to be a *lucrative* activity.)

mercenary   ADJ. interested only in the money to be gained in a situation (Arthur bought the painting for *mercenary* reasons, not because he loves art.)

nominal   ADJ. a very small price or fee (Charging only a quarter for the concert is a *nominal* admission fee.)

pawnbroker   N. someone who lends money in exchange for items that are later reclaimed or sold (He left his ring with the *pawnbroker* in exchange for ten dollars.)

peddle   V. to sell things while moving from place to place (Aneela watched the man on the street *peddle* wind-up monkeys.)

pittance   N. a very small sum of money (Because they only paid a *pittance*, Shana decided not to baby-sit for the family again.)

prosper   V. to be successful (Kevin hopes his lawn-mowing business will *prosper* so he will earn a lot of money.)

Exercise 1
Write the letter of the word that best completes the sentence.

1. Hank asked his neighbors to _____ money or books to the tutoring program.   _____
   A. donate   B. hock   C. peddle   D. acquire

2. Because of the ever-growing number of cars, the country seems to have a(n) _____
   _____ need for roads and highways.
   A. affluent   B. insatiable   C. nominal   D. clerical

3. If he cannot earn the money, he may try to _____ it some other way.
   A. peddle   B. prosper   C. hock   D. acquire   _____

4. Daniel asked the _____ how much he would lend him for the guitar.
   A. discount   B. pawnbroker   C. boom   D. depository   _____

5. Jenny can find good dresses for a(n) _____ at used clothing stores.
   A. cashier   B. interest   C. pittance   D. boom   _____

6. In a _____ job it is helpful to know how to use computers.
   A. clerical   B. mercenary   C. nominal   D. insatiable   _____

7. Jeff's dog-walking service has not been as _____ as he had hoped.
   A. insatiable   B. nominal   C. lucrative   D. clerical   _____

8. Naomi asked the principal if she could _____ her Girl Scout cookies in the
   lunchroom.
   A. acquire   B. peddle   C. prosper   D. invest   _____

9. Ryan is trying to think of a way to take advantage of the _____ in funny T-shirts.
   A. customer   B. pittance   C. pawnbroker   D. boom   _____

10. If you _____ your money wisely, you will have enough for retirement.
    A. prosper   B. peddle   C. invest   D. hock   _____

11. Because the shirt didn't have a price tag, the _____ had to check the cost.
    A. cashier   B. depository   C. pittance   D. discount   _____

12. Since his interest in the property was only _____, the buyer tore down the
    magnificent old building.
    A. clerical   B. mercenary   C. affluent   D. nominal   _____

13. We think the farm will _____ because the land is so fertile.
    A. acquire   B. invest   C. prosper   D. peddle   _____

14. Holly will try to buy her bike at a(n) _____; she doesn't want to pay full price.
    A. discount   B. interest   C. customer   D. boom   _____

15. Gina had to _____ her watch to get enough money to go to the concert.
    A. peddle   B. invest   C. prosper   D. hock   _____

Exercise 2

Write the letter of the word pair that has a relationship similar to the relationship of the
first word pair.

16. **interest : money : :**
    A. dry : dryer   C. book : page   D   _____
    B. light : dark   D. rent : land

17. **affluent : rich : :**
    A. heavy : wide   C. merry : happy   _____
    B. fast : slow   D. hand : glove

18. **depository : valuables : :**
    A. school : church   C. king : subject   _____
    B. playpen : baby   D. clock : time

19. **customer : clerk : :**
    A. patient : doctor   C. car : driver   _____
    B. color : red   D. spoon : stir

20. **nominal : large : :**
    A. quiet : noisy   C. empty : glass   _____
    B. drum : loud   D. snowy : cold

Lesson 31
Prefixes — in-/im-/ir-

All the words in this lesson contain the Latin prefixes *in-*, *im-*, or *ir-*, which mean "not."

immaturity   N. acting younger than one's age; childishness (It is a sign of her *immaturity* that she cries when she doesn't get her way.)

immodest   ADJ. lacking humility; having too much confidence (Ellen is *immodest* when she brags about her dancing ability.)

impassive   ADJ. not showing emotion (His *impassive* face gave no clue as to what he was really thinking or feeling.)

imperfection   N. a mistake or flaw (The crooked stitching on the collar was an *imperfection* in the shirt.)

impersonal   ADJ. not aimed at a particular person; lacking warmth (The *impersonal* doctor rarely smiled and did not call his patients by their first names.)

implausible   ADJ. not believable (I find it *implausible* that for three days in a row the dog has eaten your homework.)

improvisation   N. a performance given without any preparation (The students pretended they were passengers when they did their *improvisation* about riding on a bus.)

incapable   ADJ. not able or qualified to do something (Because she has been late nearly every day this year, Maggie seems *incapable* of getting to school on time.)

incognito   ADJ. with one's identity hidden; disguised (No one recognized Carrie because she went to the meeting *incognito,* wearing sunglasses and a wig.)

incongruity   N. something that is out of place or not in character (The *incongruity* of a fur coat on the hot beach made us laugh.)

inconvenience   N. something that requires extra effort or causes trouble (I will be driving past the baseball field, so it is no *inconvenience* to drop you off at practice.)

infinite   ADJ. without end or limit (On a clear night, the number of stars seems *infinite.*)

insignificant   ADJ. not important (During the investigation, even the most *insignificant* details were examined.)

invincible   ADJ. not able to be defeated (The boxer seemed *invincible* because he won every match.)

irrational   ADJ. without reason or sound judgment (Kate's *irrational* argument was too emotional and didn't make sense.)

irrelevant   ADJ. not bearing on the subject at hand (Tom's story of the bear was *irrelevant* to our conversation about tropical fish.)

irreparable   ADJ. not able to be repaired; ruined (Because the paintings can never be replaced, the fire in the museum caused *irreparable* damage.)

irresolute   ADJ. not able to make up one's mind (She is *irresolute* about whether or not to go to the dance.)

irresponsibility   N. not being reliable; untrustworthy (When he forgot to feed the hamster, Dion's mother scolded him for his *irresponsibility* toward his pet.)

irreverent   ADJ. not respectful (Talking loudly during a quiet church service is *irreverent* behavior.)

Exercise 1
Write the letter of the word that best completes the sentence.

1. There is some _____ between expressing sympathy for the homeless while eating _____ an expensive restaurant meal.
   A. incongruity   B. imperfection   C. inconvenience   D. immaturity

2. She was _____ when she laughed and told jokes at the war memorial.
      A. incognito   B. insignificant   C. irreverent   D. incapable   _____

3. The house had to be torn down after suffering _____ damage in the earthquake.
      A. invincible   B. irreparable   C. immodest   D. irrational   _____

4. The parents were surprised at the boy's _____ because he usually acted like an adult.
      A. inconvenience   B. imperfection   C. immaturity   D. incongruity   _____

5. The pencil was not valuable, so its loss is really _____.
      A. immodest   B. infinite   C. irreverent   D. insignificant   _____

6. You can never run out of counting numbers because there is a(n) _____ supply.
      A. infinite   B. irresolute   C. impersonal   D. implausible   _____

7. The theater group did a(n) _____ for our drama class.
      A. inconvenience   B. immaturity   C. imperfection   D. improvisation   _____

8. The actor always travels _____ so no one will know who he is.
      A. invincible   B. incognito   C. irresolute   D. immodest   _____

9. Having to put on boots and mittens is just one _____ of winter weather.
      A. irresponsibility   B. imperfection   C. inconvenience   D. incongruity   _____

10. The teacher's _____ manner made students think he didn't care about them.
      A. irresolute   B. infinite   C. immodest   D. impersonal   _____

Exercise 2

Write the letter of the word that most nearly has the *opposite* meaning of the italicized word.

11. *irrelevant*	A. related	B. small	C. funny	D. false	_____
12. *imperfection*	A. detail	B. front	C. flawlessness	D. confusion	_____
13. *incapable*	A. mean	B. able	C. unskilled	D. sneaky	_____
14. *irresponsibility*	A. evil	B. fairness	C. dependability	D. eagerness	_____
15. *implausible*	A. creative	B. untrue	C. believable	D. scary	_____
16. *invincible*	A. strong	B. quiet	C. tall	D. beatable	_____
17. *immodest*	A. humble	B. witty	C. grumpy	D. happy	_____
18. *irrational*	A. boring	B. sensible	C. dangerous	D. happy	_____
19. *impassive*	A. emotional	B. cruel	C. proud	D. thin	_____
20. *irresolute*	A. fearful	B. decisive	C. moderate	D. messy	_____

Lesson 32
Prefixes — after-/ante-/post-/pre-

All the words in this lesson contain the prefixes *after-*, *post-*, which mean "coming after in time"; and *ante-* and *pre-*, which mean "coming before in time."

aftereffect   N. a delayed effect (The *aftereffect* of taking the medicine was dizziness.)

afterglow   N. a pleasant feeling after a satisfying experience (For the rest of the day, Jenny basked in the *afterglow* of winning the track meet.)

aftermath   N. what happens after a disaster or misfortune (Towns lay in ruins in the *aftermath* of the hurricane.)

aftertaste   N. a taste left in the mouth after the substance which caused it is no longer there (The sweet liquid left a bitter *aftertaste* in John's mouth.)

afterthought   N. a thought coming later, or too late (As an *afterthought,* she added the hat to her purchases.)

antecedent   N. an event that comes before another (The invention of radio was an *antecedent* to the development of television.)

anteroom   N. waiting room (Daniel waited nervously with the other patients in the *anteroom* of the dentist's office.)

postdate   V. to put a later date on a check or letter (If you *postdate* the letter, she will think you wrote it tomorrow.)

posterity   N. those who come after; future generations (We can help *posterity* by cleaning up the environment.)

posthaste   ADV. rapidly, with great speed (Since he had been told to deliver the letter *posthaste,* he ran all the way.)

postlude   N. a piece of music played at the end of a ceremony or composition (As the organ played the *postlude,* the people began to leave the church.)

postscript   N. a short message added to a letter that has already been signed (She added a few sentences to the letter in a *postscript* below her signature.)

precedent   N. something that can be used as an example later (If you don't punish him for being late, it might set a *precedent* for times when he is late again.)

precook   V. to cook in advance (Before grilling the ribs, *precook* them in boiling water.)

preempt   V. to appropriate or seize beforehand; to replace (The President's speech will *preempt* the program that usually comes on at this time.)

prelude   N. a piece of music that comes at the beginning of a ceremony or composition (The orchestra played the *prelude* before the curtain rose.)

prepackage   V. to wrap before it goes to market (If you *prepackage* the candy bars in boxes of four, people will not be able to buy just one bar.)

pretext   N. a false reason used to hide a true one (His *pretext* for going out was to return a library book, but what he really wanted was an ice cream cone.)

prevent   V. to keep from happening (If you can *prevent* your sister from seeing the popcorn, she won't ask for any.)

preview   V. to look at in advance (The critics will *preview* the film before it is offered to the public.)

Exercise 1
Write the letter of the word that best completes the sentence.

1. In the _____ to the letter Jane encouraged me to write back.   _____
   A. posterity   B. postscript   C. postlude   D. afterglow

2. The strange _____ of the lemonade made him wonder if a drug had been put into   _____
   his drink.
   A. aftermath   B. afterthought   C. postlude   D. aftertaste

3. She will _____ the television program before she lets her children watch it.   _____
   A. prevent   B. precook   C. preview   D. postdate

4. The _____ to the protest march was a small rally in the town square.   _____
   A. postscript   B. antecedent   C. pretext   D. postlude

5. The beans will be more tender if you _____ them before adding them to the salad.   _____
   A. precook   B. prepackage   C. postdate   D. preview

6. Tyrone felt warm and happy in the _____ of his opening night performance.   _____
   A. antecedent   B. aftermath   C. postdate   D. afterglow

7. One _____ of too much jogging can be leg cramps.   _____
   A. afterthought   B. postscript   C. aftereffect   D. precedent

8. On the first day of school the teacher set a _____ for dealing with misbehavior by   _____
   writing names on the board and having those students stay after school.
   A. pretext   B. precedent   C. anteroom   D. aftereffect

9. Harry called his girlfriend on the _____ of wanting to know the homework   _____
   assignment.
   A. aftereffect   B. posterity   C. postscript   D. pretext

10. In the _____ of the war, many people were without food and shelter.   _____
    A. aftermath   B. anteroom   C. antecedent   D. prelude

11. As a(n) _____, he added an extra cookie to his sack lunch.   _____
    A. prelude   B. aftertaste   C. afterglow   D. afterthought

12. The orchestra began to play the _____ and Ann knew the concert was almost over.   _____
    A. prelude   B. postlude   C. antecedent   D. precedent

13. Gordon will _____ the check so it cannot be cashed until a later date.   _____
    A. preview   B. prevent   C. postdate   D. precook

14. Because he is friend of the property owner, Mr. Welch's bid for that piece of real   _____
    estate is likely to _____ all other bids.
    A. preview   B. postdate   C. preempt   D. pretext

15. At the grocery store they _____ vegetables by wrapping them in cellophane.   _____
    A. precook   B. prepackage   C. preempt   D. preview

Exercise 2

Write the letter of the word that has a relationship that is similar to the first word pair.

16. **posthaste : swiftly : :**   A. sky : blue   C. damp : moist   _____
                                    B. king : subject   D. up : down

17. **prelude : opera : :**   A. paint : brush   C. soil : seed   _____
                                    B. foreword : novel   D. bake : cookie

18. **anteroom : wait : :**   A. bedroom : sleep   C. horse : saddle   _____
                                    B. grass : field   D. kitchen : sink

19. **posterity : forefathers : :** A. children : teacher C. see : eye   _____
                                    B. happy : glad   D. heirs : ancestors

20. **prevent : prevention : :**   A. weigh : weight   C. go : went   _____
                                    B. care : careful   D. rise : risen

Lesson 33
Clothing

All the words in this lesson may be associated with clothing.

accessory   N. an extra thing added to something of more importance (Carla bought a gold belt as an *accessory* for the green dress.)

allure   N. attraction or charm (The *allure* of the expensive clothing store was so great that the boy went in, even though he knew he could not buy anything.)

bedeck   V. to decorate or adorn (In times of old, girls would *bedeck* themselves with flowers for the spring festival.)

disarray   N. lack of order; confusion (The house was in *disarray* the morning after the wild party.)

dungaree   N. a rough cloth made of cotton that is used for work clothes (Ralph wore the jeans made of blue *dungaree* for painting.)

durable   ADJ. able to withstand wear (Parachutes are made of a *durable* fabric that will not tear or rot.)

elegant   ADJ. tasteful and refined (The *elegant* dress was simple, yet it looked expensive.)

embroider   V. to add details to cloth with a stitched pattern (Mother will use blue thread to *embroider* my initials on the shirt collar.)

excess   N. beyond the usual amount; too much; more than enough (After you have used as much fabric as you need, store the *excess* in the chest.)

hem   V. to fold over and sew down an edge of cloth (A wider *hem* will shorten the skirt.)

immaculate   ADJ. perfectly clean; without a stain (Although his shirt was *immaculate* in the morning, by afternoon it was covered with dirt.)

incongruous   ADJ. incompatible; lacking in harmony (The necktie looked *incongruous* with the shorts.)

keepsake   N. a thing kept in memory of the person who gave it (My father's high school jacket is a *keepsake* I will always cherish.)

ludicrous   ADJ. laughable; ridiculous (It is *ludicrous* to think the seventh grader could squeeze into his five year-old brother's jacket.)

ornamental   ADJ. used to add beauty or decoration (The button on the dress is only *ornamental* and serves no useful purpose.)

rayon   N. an artificial fabric used to make lightweight clothing (Many summer clothes are made from *rayon* because it is light and cool.)

satin   N. a kind of cloth with a very smooth, glossy side (The *satin* shirt felt cool and slippery on his skin.)

seamstress   N. a person whose work is sewing (Instead of buying a dress for the dance, Linda paid a *seamstress* to make one.)

simplicity   N. lack of complexity or elaborateness (She disliked frills and ruffles, preferring the *simplicity* of a plain black dress.)

spin   V. to make thread or yarn by drawing out and twisting cotton, wool, or other fibers (My grandmother would use sheep's wool to *spin* her own yarn.)

Exercise 1
Write the letter of the word pair that best completes the sentence.

1. The necklace she wore as a(n) _____ was a(n) _____ from her mother.   _____
   A. allure — rayon
   B. accessory — allure
   C. accessory — keepsake
   D. keepsake — allure

2. The _____ of the _____ outfit was so great that she bought it without hesitation.   _____
   A. allure — elegant
   B. excess — elegant
   C. satin — elegant
   D. rayon — immaculate

3. When he found the pants were too long, he asked a _____ to _____ them.   _____
   A. dungaree — bedeck
   B. seamstress — bedeck
   C. seamstress — hem
   D. keepsake — embroider

4. The blue _____ was a(n) _____ fabric that lasted for years.   _____
   A. rayon — immaculate
   B. dungaree — durable
   C. satin — ludicrous
   D. dungaree — ornamental

5. After playing football, the _____ shirt was covered with mud and his good clothes   _____
   were in _____.
   A. immaculate — disarray
   B. durable — allure
   C. ornamental — excess
   D. rayon — simplicity

6. For the royal ball, the queen will _____ herself in _____ and other fine fabrics.   _____
   A. embroider — keepsake
   B. spin — rayon
   C. bedeck — satin
   D. hem — satin

7. A(n) _____ of jewelry will ruin the _____ of the dress.   _____
   A. allure — rayon
   B. excess — simplicity
   C. disarray — keepsake
   D. accessory — dungaree

8. With this thread, you can _____ a(n) _____ design on the shawl.   _____
   A. spin — immaculate
   B. hem — ludicrous
   C. bedeck — incongruous
   D. embroider — ornamental

9. It seemed _____ to see the woman _____ flax into cloth in the middle of the   _____
   city street.
   A. durable — embroider
   B. elegant — hem
   C. immaculate — spin
   D. incongruous — spin

10. It is _____ to go out in the cold wearing only a shirt made of _____.   _____
    A. immaculate — satin
    B. ornamental — dungaree
    C. ludicrous — rayon
    D. elegant — allure

Exercise 2
Write the letter of the word that most nearly has the *same* meaning as the italicized
word.

11. *immaculate*	A. different	B. drab	C. spotless	D. kind	_____
12. *durable*	A. messy	B. short	C. strong	D. small	_____
13. *ornamental*	A. loud	B. neat	C. plain	D. decorative	_____
14. *accessory*	A. supplement	B. stripe	C. sweater	D. length	_____
15. *ludicrous*	A. normal	B. absurd	C. good	D. alive	_____
16. *incongruous*	A. clashing	B. low	C. small	D. pleasant	_____
17. *seamstress*	A. question	B. waiter	C. stitcher	D. needle	_____
18. *simplicity*	A. group	B. plainness	C. thread	D. location	_____
19. *disarray*	A. disorder	B. collar	C. change	D. shape	_____
20. *allure*	A. attitude	B. tale	C. help	D. pull	_____

Lesson 34
Nature

All the words in this lesson may be associated with nature.

abundant ADJ. available in large amounts; plentiful (Squirrels like this part of the park because of the *abundant* supply of acorns.)

bramble N. a thorny bush or vine (Her arms and legs were scratched as she pushed her way through the *bramble* in the woods.)

camouflage V. to disguise or hide by looking like the background (The brown moth is able to *camouflage* itself by sitting still on dry leaves.)

changeable ADJ. not likely to remain the same (The *changeable* spring weather can turn from sunny to cloudy without warning.)

conceal V. to hide or cover (You cannot see the opening to the cave because thick bushes *conceal* it.)

deprive V. to prevent from having; to withhold (The lack of rain will *deprive* the plants of the water they need.)

extricate V. to release from; to rescue (Juan worked to *extricate* the lion cub that was entangled in the net.)

fledgling N. a baby bird that has just learned to fly (Since the bird was just a *fledgling,* it could not yet fly long distances.)

fragrant ADJ. having a pleasing smell (Yvonne enjoyed the *fragrant* perfume of the spring lilacs.)

havoc N. extreme damage and destruction (In the night, the raccoons had played *havoc* with our trash, which was now spread all over the yard.)

heather N. a small evergreen shrub with pinkish-purple flowers (The distant hills, covered with *heather,* looked purple in the sunlight.)

inhabit V. to live in a place (Pigeons *inhabit* the ledges on the school building.)

landscape V. to plant trees, flowers, etc.; to improve the look of a place (The city plans to *landscape* the park by planting a grove of pine trees and adding a rose garden.)

lavender ADJ. a light bluish purple (The sky was *lavender* just after sundown.)

misty ADJ. clouded by fine water droplets (Her face felt damp as she walked through the *misty* air of the early morning fog.)

nocturnal ADJ. active at night (The owl wakes up at sundown because it is a *nocturnal* hunter.)

pastoral ADJ. having to do with the simple life in the country (No cars or motorized vehicles disturbed the *pastoral* calm of the summer cabin.)

scenic ADJ. beautiful; nice to look at (We took the *scenic* route so we could enjoy the countryside.)

sparse ADJ. in short supply; scanty (There were few deer in the area because of the *sparse* grass for grazing.)

thistle N. a prickly plant with a large purple flower (Her hand was covered with tiny stickers after she brushed against the *thistle.*)

Exercise 1

Write the letter of the word set that best completes the sentence.

1. Leroy likes to take long walks through the _____ on _____ days. _____
   A. havoc — fragrant   C. bramble — nocturnal
   B. fledgling — sparse   D. heather — misty

2. The violent storm played _____ with the forest and will _____ many animals of   _____
   their homes.
   A. heather — landscape   C. havoc — deprive
   B. havoc — inhabit   D. bramble — extricate

3. The green and purple dragonfly can _____ itself on the _____. _____
   A. landscape — fledgling
   B. camouflage — thistle
   C. inhabit — havoc
   D. extricate — bramble

4. Because bats are _____, they _____ themselves during the day. _____
   A. scenic — deprive
   B. nocturnal — conceal
   C. changeable — inhabit
   D. nocturnal — deprive

5. The grazing cows and _____ flowers were part of the _____ scene. _____
   A. misty — changeable
   B. lavender — nocturnal
   C. sparse — abundant
   D. lavender — pastoral

6. A gardener has been hired to _____ the grounds to make them more _____. _____
   A. landscape — scenic
   B. inhabit — changeable
   C. deprive — fragrant
   D. conceal — pastoral

7. The rose blossoms are _____ this year, but they are as _____ as ever. _____
   A. misty — lavender
   B. sparse — fragrant
   C. nocturnal — pastoral
   D. lavender — misty

8. Watch for thorns when you try to _____ the frisbee from the _____. _____
   A. deprive — havoc
   B. inhabit — thistle
   C. extricate — bramble
   D. camouflage — heather

9. The number of ducks on the pond is _____, but right now there is a(n) _____ _____
   flock.
   A. nocturnal — scenic
   B. changeable — abundant
   C. sparse — fragrant
   D. scenic — changeable

10. The _____ is ready to leave the nest and _____ another part of the woods. _____
    A. fledgling — inhabit
    B. heather — landscape
    C. fledgling — deprive
    D. fledgling — conceal

Exercise 2

Write the letter of the word that most nearly has the *opposite* meaning of the italicized word.

11. *havoc*	A. field	B. calm	C. shell	D. disorder	_____
12. *extricate*	A. lift	B. escape	C. burrow	D. entangle	_____
13. *conceal*	A. hide	B. support	C. reveal	D. listen	_____
14. *scenic*	A. pretty	B. unsightly	C. high	D. wooded	_____
15. *abundant*	A. many	B. heavy	C. moist	D. few	_____
16. *deprive*	A. provide	B. burn	C. chase	D. destroy	_____
17. *changeable*	A. hollow	B. muddy	C. fixed	D. spooky	_____
18. *sparse*	A. dry	B. plentiful	C. few	D. rocky	_____
19. *misty*	A. foggy	B. chilly	C. clear	D. sunny	_____
20. *pastoral*	A. far	B. urban	C. quiet	D. musical	_____

Lesson 35
Suffixes — -ate/-en/-fy/-ize

All the words in this lesson contain the suffixes *-ate, -en, -fy,* or *-ize* which mean "to make."

activate V. to put in motion (When it was time for lift-off, the control room ordered the astronaut to *activate* the rocket engine.)

beautify V. to make beautiful or attractive (Wildflowers help *beautify* our highways.)

computerize V. to put onto a computer system (When we *computerize* the school office, all attendance records will be kept on the computer instead of in file cabinets.)

deafen V. to make unable to hear (Working around loud equipment without earplugs can *deafen* a person.)

falsify V. to change in order to deceive (It is illegal to *falsify* a driver's license by changing the date of birth.)

finalize V. to make finished (We need one more signature to *finalize* the contract.)

fortify V. to protect a place against attack (Kings used to *fortify* their castles by placing canons in the towers.)

frighten V. to make afraid; scare (Don't *frighten* your sister by making weird noises at night.)

harmonize V. to bring into agreement or accord (The colors of the furniture *harmonize* because beige and red go well together.)

itemize V. to list each entry (Please *itemize* the groceries we need and take the list to the store.)

loosen V. to unfasten or make looser (If your necktie is too tight, you should *loosen* it.)

minimize V. to make the least of (If you are careful, you will *minimize* the chances of having an accident.)

pulsate V. to beat or throb (He could hear the drum beats *pulsate* in his head.)

rationalize V. to make up reasons for one's actions or failures (She tried to *rationalize* her low test grade by saying that getting a bad grade would make her work harder.)

realize V. to understand clearly (I can see by your face that you *realize* the danger we are in.)

simplify V. to make easier or less complex (Please *simplify* the story when you tell it to the kindergarten class.)

strengthen V. to make stronger (Lifting weights will help *strengthen* your arms and legs.)

terrify V. to fill with great fear (Turning off all the lights at night will *terrify* the young child.)

vacillate V. to move indecisively from one alternative to another (While you *vacillate* between whether to go or to stay, the bus may leave without you.)

validate V. to support by facts or authority (In our English class, we must *validate* each argument with reasons.)

Exercise 1
Write the letter of the word that best completes the sentence.

1. After our course in European history, we began to _____ how unique the U. S. constitution really is.   _____
    A. minimize   B. pulsate   C. simplify   D. realize

2. The boys' club helped _____ their city by picking up the roadside trash.   _____
    A. deafen   B. realize   C. beautify   D. vacillate

3. By the end of the night, the committee was able to _____ plans for the annual
   fund-raiser.   _____
   A. finalize   B. loosen   C. frighten   D. realize

4. The girl tried to _____ the school I.D. card by substituting someone else's picture.   _____
   A. fortify   B. falsify   C. harmonize   D. pulsate

5. The sales clerk had to _____ each piece of clothing on the customer's receipt.   _____
   A. itemize   B. frighten   C. strengthen   D. activate

6. After the race, John could feel his heart _____ rapidly.   _____
   A. pulsate   B. vacillate   C. fortify   D. beautify

7. The song called for three voices to _____ during the chorus.   _____
   A. validate   B. minimize   C. harmonize   D. beautify

8. The girl tried to _____ stealing the book by saying that the store would not miss it. _____
   A. terrify   B. rationalize   C. deafen   D. frighten

9. You only have five minutes for the true-false test, so don't _____ between the   _____
   choices for long.
   A. realize   B. minimize   C. harmonize   D. vacillate

10. A newspaper reporter must always _____ the story by making sure his sources   _____
    were telling the truth.
    A. validate   B. vacillate   C. pulsate   D. beautify

11. Doctors now believe that listening to loud music may temporarily _____ a person.   _____
    A. harmonize   B. rationalize   C. finalize   D. deafen

12. If you _____ the dog's collar too much, it might come off.   _____
    A. falsify   B. itemize   C. loosen   D. simplify

13. Loud thunder during a rainstorm can _____ even a brave adult.   _____
    A. terrify   B. validate   C. loosen   D. beautify

14. The gymnast worked each day to _____ the muscles in her shoulders.   _____
    A. deafen   B. strengthen   C. vacillate   D. finalize

15. A safety rope is used to _____ the danger in the sport of rock climbing.   _____
    A. rationalize   B. frighten   C. finalize   D. minimize

Exercise 2

Write the letter of the word pair that has a relationship similar to the relationship of the
first word pair.

16. *frighten : scare : :*   A. first : last   C. soap : clean   _____
                                 B. far : distant   D. pen : write

17. *activate : stop : :*   A. old : young   C. she : her   _____
                                 B. meat : beef   D. finger : hand

18. *computerize : computer : :* A. smooth : smoother   C. child : children   _____
                                 B. time : watch   D. automate : machine

19. *fortify : weapons : :*   A. much : little   C. build : tools   _____
                                 B. book : character   D. open : unlock

20. *simplify : easier : :*   A. write : pencil   C. happy : sad   _____
                                 B. lock : safer   D. run : trot

Lesson 36
Suffixes — -ance/-ence/-dom/-ity

All the words in this lesson contain the suffixes *-ance*, *-ence*, *-dom,* or *-ity* which mean "state or quality of."

abhorrence N. a feeling of great hatred (His *abhorrence* of bloodshed causes him to avoid violent movies.)

ability N. being able to do something (Because he is well-coordinated, he has the *ability* to be a good athlete.)

absence N. the state of being away (Marie's *absence* from school caused her to fall behind in her lessons.)

assurance N. self-confidence (She has studied geology, so she can speak with *assurance* when she talks about rocks.)

avoidance N. keeping away from (Her *avoidance* of desserts will help her lose weight.)

dependence N. a trust or reliance on another for support (Her *dependence* on her older brother keeps her from doing things on her own.)

finality N. the condition of being final or settled (The *finality* in her voice made me know she would not change her mind.)

hilarity N. noisy cheerfulness (The surprise appearance of a stray dog in the classroom caused great *hilarity* among the students.)

insurance N. payment for protection of property, person, or life (After the house burned down, the owner's *insurance* paid for the damage.)

kingdom N. the land ruled by a king or queen (The king collected taxes from everyone in the *kingdom.*)

martyrdom N. the death or suffering of one because of his or her religion or beliefs (The people remembered the *martyrdom* of the political leader who had given her life for the revolution.)

necessity N. that which cannot be done without (Air is a *necessity* for human life.)

passivity N. lack of reaction in the face of some other action (People wondered at the man's *passivity* as he let himself be led away by the police.)

relevance N. being connected to the matter at hand (The paragraph about whales had no *relevance* to the essay topic of farming.)

reluctance N. unwillingness (His *reluctance* to take chances made him a very cautious person.)

repentance N. sorrow for having done wrong (The criminal wept as he expressed *repentance* for his past mistakes.)

stardom N. being a popular or highly regarded performer (The young actor's *stardom* brought him fame and fortune.)

vanity N. too much pride in one's looks or abilities (His *vanity* would not let him pass a mirror without admiring himself.)

violence N. rough force or harmful action (The *violence* of the hurricane destroyed buildings and flooded towns.)

wisdom N. knowledge and good judgement based on experience (A good teacher possesses *wisdom* that cannot be learned in a book.)

Exercise 1
Write the letter of the word that best completes the sentence.

1. The small _____ was ruled by an evil queen.   _____
   A. insurance   B. kingdom   C. violence   D. relevance

2. After breaking the window, the girl expressed _____, saying she was sorry.   _____
   A. repentance   B. vanity   C. hilarity   D. avoidance

3. Jill's natural musical _____ will help her become a good piano player. _____
   A. martyrdom   B. stardom   C. dependence   D. ability

4. A low turnout on election day may reflect voters' _____ about the issues. _____
   A. passivity   B. relevance   C. finality   D. ability

5. John's _____ of lakes and swimming pools indicated that he was afraid of the _____
   water.
   A. absence   B. necessity   C. avoidance   D. wisdom

6. His brilliant playing suggested that the young violinist was headed for _____. _____
   A. kingdom   B. stardom   C. reluctance   D. abhorrence

7. There was much _____ when the host did his imitation of the mayor. _____
   A. assurance   B. passivity   C. hilarity   D. repentance

8. His strange question had little _____ to the subject of our discussion. _____
   A. stardom   B. finality   C. absence   D. relevance

9. Some people believe that _____ is the highest contribution one can make to a _____
   cause.
   A. insurance   B. passivity   C. vanity   D. martyrdom

10. Her _____ paid for all damages to her car in the accident. _____
    A. insurance   B. abhorrence   C. violence   D. wisdom

Exercise 2

Write the letter of the word that most nearly has the *opposite* meaning as the italicized word.

11. *wisdom*	A. foolishness	B. skill	C. need	D. problem	_____
12. *reluctance*	A. story	B. hatred	C. desire	D. bottom	_____
13. *assurance*	A. appearance	B. uncertainty	C. lock	D. goal	_____
14. *abhorrence*	A. ridicule	B. love	C. group	D. change	_____
15. *dependence*	A. evening	B. stand	C. win	D. freedom	_____
16. *violence*	A. gentleness	B. tension	C. question	D. harm	_____
17. *absence*	A. mistake	B. friendship	C. attendance	D. desk	_____
18. *vanity*	A. strength	B. humility	C. favor	D. kindness	_____
19. *finality*	A. end	B. belief	C. total	D. indecision	_____
20. *necessity*	A. luxury	B. globe	C. try	D. library	_____

ANSWER KEY

Spelling Development

Spelling Master 1
Pages 1–2

Practice the Words
Answers will vary. Possible answers are given.
1. placing
2. wasting
3. requirement
4. naming
5. improving
6. sincerity
7. forgiveness
8. hoping
9. separating
10. involving

Apply What You Know
1. maturity
2. creatively
3. believable
4. revision
5. continuous
6. scarcely
7. amazement
8. cultural
9. careful
10. insurance

Proofreading Practice

DODGEING DUMB DARES

Are you troubled by friends dareing you to do mean or dangerous things like teasing kids or stealing valueables? What would you do if these kinds of dares were a requirment for getting into a special club or "cool" crowd; here are some useable strategies for ignoring a dare without loseing a friend or causing an arguement. Try making up an excuse, changeing the subject, or walking away. Better yet, stand up for what is write or point out the stupidity of engaging in dangerous activities.

Spelling Master 2
Pages 3–4

Practice the Words
1. counties
2. emptying
3. journeys
4. sprayed
5. replied
6. enjoying
7. balconies
8. displaying
9. holidays
10. steadying

Apply What You Know
1. surveys, surveyed, surveying
2. envy, envies, envied
3. stays, stayed, staying
4. multiplies, multiplied, multiplying
5. satisfy, satisfies, satisfying
6. pities, pitied, pitying
7. relay, relayed, relaying
8. annoys, annoyed, annoying
9. notifies, notified, notifying
10. carry, carries, carried

Proofreading Practice

Do you want to earn more money as a baby sitter and have your choice of the most envyable jobs in the neighborhood? If so, learn to improve your skills by taking the baby-sitting course at Mercy hospital. The saturday morning classes are held in laboratoryes and taught by certifed instructors. You will learn about child safety and baby-sitting procedures, including lessons on how babys should be carryed, when parents should be notified, what to do when emergences arise, and how to entertain kids. The course are open to boys and girls ages twelve to sixteen.

Spelling Master 3
Pages 5–6

Practice the Words

1. saddest	6. darning
2. dimly	7. planning
3. seated	8. waiting
4. chairing	9. slippery
5. starred	10. sleepy

a. seated	f. slippery
b. darning	g. dimly
c. starred	h. Sleepy
d. waiting	i. chairing
e. saddest	j. planned

Apply What You Know

Across	Down
2. grabbed	1. meeting
6. stirring	3. robber
8. turning	4. biggest
9. fatten	5. shipped
10. stopped	7. shooting
12. skirting	10. swimmer
13. jogger	11. pinned
14. baggage	

Proofreading Practice

While spiting may be impolite for humans, it is actually a survival skill for many animals. One kind of cobra, for instance, can spit its venom into the face of an enemy standing eight feet away! Adult archerfish can spit even farther. Swiming just under the surface, these fish are experts at spoting bugs on plants, shooting a stream of water at the bugs, and then catching the bugs in their mouths In turn, "walking worms" catch insects by squirtling a slime over them The slime hardens into a cage. Camels and llamas will spit right in the face of anyone who upset them so watch out for these animals or you may get zaped!

Spelling Master 4
Pages 7–8

Practice the Words

1. visitor
2. equipment
3. offering
4. beginner
5. reference
6. suffering
7. conferring
8. rebellion
9. committee
10. differing

Apply What You Know

con trol'   pi' lot   re fer'   pro pel'
for get'   pre fer'   hap' pen   trans mit'

1. propeller
2. transmittal
3. referral
4. preference
5. piloting
6. forgettable
7. happening
8. controller

Proofreading Practice

In 1989 the space Shuttle *Atlantis* propeled the *Magellan* toward Venus. The *Magellan* differed from other spacecraft that had orbited Venus, before 1989 because it transmited radar images of Venus's surface more clear than the others did. These images showed that Venus is covered with volcanoes. Scientists think that magma expeled from the volcanoes is responsible for the spidery formations seen on Venus and not seen on other planets.

Spelling Master 5
Pages 9–10

Practice the Words
1. invention
2. consequence
3. prevention
4. suburban
5. exclaim
6. conclude
7. include
8. propose
9. recommend
10. exclude

Apply What You Know
Answers will vary. Possible answers are given.
1. deserve, preserve, reserve, conserve; base word
2. resist, insist, consist; root
3. detect, protect; root
4. deform, reform, inform, conform; base word
5. decode; base word
6. request, inquest, conquest; base word
7. deject, reject, inject, project; root
8. predict, indict; root
9. depart; base word
10. prolong; base word

Proofreading Practice

To ~~ik~~^{ex}splore the deep ocean, scientists needed

an ~~e~~ⁱnvention that could pr^{er}~~e~~form under harsh

conditions and for pr^o~~e~~longed periods of time. It

would have to p^{ro}~~e~~vide air, light, pressurization, and

communication. The result was a small submarine

name ~~a~~^dlvin. *Alvin* holds three passengers and

subm~~m~~erges to depths of 7,500 feet. It allows

scientists to explore a previously ~~e~~^uncharted

frontier.

Spelling Master 6
Pages 11–12

Practice the Words
Answers and word choices will vary. Possible answers provided.
1. I thought the <u>editorial</u> was well written.
2. Yes, he is my mother's <u>relative</u>.
3. A <u>grammatical</u> mistake would result.
4. Citizens in a <u>democratic</u> society have a responsibility to vote.
5. A person can gain <u>confidence</u> by believing he or she is valuable and loved.
6. I think chimpanzees have the most <u>human</u> expressions and actions.
7. The best <u>remedy</u> is to drink lots of fluids and get plenty of sleep.
8. I think I am in the mood for a <u>comedy</u>.
9. Her <u>hostility</u> is a result of an argument they had last week.
10. It may have seemed like a <u>fantasy</u> a hundred years ago, but now it seems very possible.

Apply What You Know
1. bi ol' o gy; bi o log' i cal
2. an' gel; an gel' ic
3. phi los' o phy; phil o soph' ic
4. in' fi nite; in fin' i ty
5. mol' e cule; mo lec' u lar
6. spon ta' ne ous; spon ta ne' i ty
7. ge og' ra phy; ge o graph' i cal
8. im' pro vise; im prov i sa' tion

Proofreading Practice

Last week I went to an improv~~a~~ⁱsational comedy

club called The Funny Place. It is a place where

young com~~f~~edians perform humorous skits. One

skit was about a student studying human anat~~a~~^omy

in a biol~~e~~^ogy class. The jokes and the expressions

~~was~~^{were} hilarious! Speaking of classes, I am really

starting to like my geogr~~o~~^aphy class. Ever since I

went to visit my rel~~i~~^atives in Mexico, I have taken a

greater interest in learning about foreign countries.

I just remembered I have a gramm~~e~~^ar quiz tomorrow,

so I better start studying. I hope to hear from you

soon.

Spelling Master 7
Pages 13–14

Practice the Words
The first word in each pair should be circled. The second word is the spelling word. The sentences that expand each phrase will vary.
 1. small; slight
 2. touring; sightseeing
 3. completely; thoroughly
 4. octogenerian; eightieth
 5. though; although
 6. girl; daughter
 7. all over; throughout
 8. should; ought
 9. measured; weighed
10. elevation; height

Apply What You Know
 1. mighty
 2. neighborhood
 3. copyright
 4. frightened
 5. delightful

Proofreading Practice

    WANTED: Tommy the Terrible, a thoro~~u~~ghly thaughtless thief w~~ei~~ghing 180 pounds, is wanted for robbery. Tommy f~~au~~ught his way out of the ~~C~~ounty ~~jail~~ And may be living in ~~you're~~ your n~~ei~~ghborhood. A reward is offer~~f~~ed for information leading to his arrest.

    STOLEN: The Eig~~h~~th Wonder of the World Tour Company ~~have~~ has reported that ~~there site-seeing~~ their sightseeing bus has been stole~~n~~. A search thr~~ough~~out the county should be made. Contact Ms. Page, the owner's d~~au~~ughter, for more details.

Spelling Master 8
Pages 15–16

Practice the Words
 1. visible
 2. manageable
 3. edible
 4. noticeable
 5. regrettable
 6. agreeable
 7. available
 8. audible
 9. advisable
10. legible

Apply What You Know
 1. adapt; adaptable
 2. control; controllable
 3. cred; credible
 4. change; changeable
 5. tang; tangible

Proofreading Practice

    Many companies claim that their packages are not harmful to the environment, but how do you know if those claims are cred~~a~~ible? First, remember that a truly biodegrad~~e~~able product is one that is perish~~i~~able, like a banana peel. Air, sunlight, and moisture must be available to break substances down. Thus, products like ~~D~~ispos~~e~~able diapers that are dumped in landfills and covered with garbage can't decompose. Second, many items that are said to be recycl~~e~~able are rarely recycled. So check whether a product is accept~~i~~able in your area before you buy it. It's not recyclable if there ~~are~~ is no place for you to recycle it.

Spelling Master 9
Pages 17–18

Practice the Words
1. genius
2. despise
3. adventurous
4. advertise
5. criticize
6. courageous
7. surplus
8. outrageous
9. virus
10. sympathize
11. televise
12. apologize

Apply What You Know

Has a Suffix	Does Not Have a Suffix
civilize	bonus
continuous	exercise
customize	compromise
momentous	concise
mischievous	census

Proofreading Practice

Circus Extravaganza!

March 22-31

PBS, Channel 11

Circus Extravaganza, a nationally televi*s*ed circus,

features co*u*ragous lion tamers gorg*e*ous horses,

mischi*e*vous monkeys, and a charmer of poison*o*us

snakes!

Don't miss it!

Customised stationery

Consultants

We specialized in personalised envelopes and

writing paper for the home and office. Call one of

our sales representatives for a free brochure!

555-3624

Spelling Master 10
Pages 19–20

Practice the Words
1. descendant
2. attendance
3. science
4. ancient
5. defendant
6. annoyance
7. inhabitant
8. efficient
9. frequent
10. sequence
11. defiance
12. conscience

Apply What You Know
1. avoidance
2. sufficient
3. crescent
4. appliance
5. contestant
6. delinquent
7. adolescence
8. triumphant

Proofreading Practice

PLANET OF THE GRAPES

The Bacchians, anc*a*ent inhabit*a*nts of the planet

bacchus act in defi*a*nce of the law by imprisoning

the cresent-shaped creatures known as The Grape

Eaters.

AS THE WORLD ERUPTS

A new science program on how we can safely and

efficiently harnassed the energy from volcanic

eruptions to power our electrical appliances.

Vocabulary Development

Lesson 1 Cuisine
Pages 21–22

Exercise 1

1. C	6. D
2. B	7. C
3. A	8. A
4. D	9. B
5. B	10. D

Exercise 2

11. B	14. C	17. C	20. B
12. A	15. B	18. B	
13. D	16. C	19. A	

Lesson 2 Sports
Pages 23–24

Exercise 1

1. C	6. D	11. B
2. D	7. B	12. C
3. A	8. D	13. D
4. B	9. B	14. C
5. A	10. A	15. A

Exercise 2

16. C *Extremely* is a synonym of *very; fast* is a synonym of *quickly.*
17. A *Flexible* is an antonym for *stiff; happy* is an antonym for *sad.*
18. B *Compete* is the verb and *competition* is the noun; *attend* is the verb and *attention* is the noun.
19. C You *defend* a goal; you *attack* an enemy.
20. C A *uniform* is worn on a *body;* a *shoe* is worn on a *foot.*

Lesson 3 Performing Arts
Pages 25-26

Exercise 1

1. B	6. A	11. A
2. C	7. C	12. B
3. A	8. D	13. D
4. C	9. A	14. C
5. A	10. D	15. B

Exercise 2

16. B A *dramatist* creates a *play;* an *author* creates a *book.*
17. A A *villain* acts *mean;* a *policeman* acts *helpful.*
18. D *Hilarious* is a synonym for *funny; big* is a synonym for *large.*
19. C A *spectator* will *view* something; a *driver* will *steer* something.
20. D A *professional* performs for *money;* an *amateur* performs for *free.*

Lesson 4 Transportation
Pages 27–28

Exercise 1

1. C	5. C	9. C	13. B
2. D	6. B	10. A	14. C
3. B	7. D	11. D	15. A
4. A	8. B	12. C	

Exercise 2

16. B As you *accelerate,* you increase *speed;* as you *grow,* you increase *height.*
17. D A *chauffeur* operates a *car;* a *pilot* operates an *airplane.*
18. B *Economical* is an antonym of *wasteful; real* is an antonym of *imaginary.*
19. C *Various* is the adjective and *variety* is the noun; *wintery* is the adjective and *winter* is the noun.
20. A A *radiator* cools an *engine; ice* cools a *beverage.*

Lesson 5 Social Studies
Pages 29–30

Exercise 1

1. C	5. C	9. D	13. D
2. D	6. A	10. B	14. A
3. A	7. C	11. D	15. C
4. B	8. B	12. B	

Exercise 2

16. B *Resignation* is the noun and *resign* is the verb; *action* is the noun and *act* is the verb.
17. A *Truce* is an antonym of *fight; stop* is an antonym of *start.*
18. D You *manufacture toys;* you *cook food.*
19. B *Unite* is a synonym of *combine; quick* is a synonym of *fast.*
20. D A *jury* is made up of *people;* an *army* is made up of *soldiers.*

Lesson 6 Human Behavior
Pages 31–32

Exercise 1

1. B	6. C
2. A	7. B
3. C	8. A
4. B	9. D
5. D	10. C

Exercise 2

11. B	16. A
12. D	17. D
13. A	18. C
14. B	19. B
15. C	20. D

Lesson 7 Human Behavior
Pages 33–34

Exercise 1

1. D	6. D
2. B	7. A
3. A	8. C
4. B	9. B
5. C	10. D

Exercise 2

11. A	14. C	17. B	20. A
12. B	15. A	18. D	
13. D	16. C	19. C	

Lesson 8 The Desert
Pages 35–36

Exercise 1

1. B	6. D
2. D	7. A
3. B	8. C
4. A	9. B
5. C	10. D

Exercise 2

11. A	14. B	17. A	20. A
12. C	15. D	18. B	
13. D	16. D	19. C	

Lesson 9 Geography
Pages 37–38

Exercise 1

1. B	6. A
2. D	7. B
3. C	8. C
4. A	9. A
5. C	10. B

Exercise 2

11. C	14. A	17. A	20. C
12. A	15. C	18. D	
13. B	16. C	19. A	

Lesson 10 Feelings
Pages 39–40

Exercise 1

1. D	6. A
2. A	7. C
3. B	8. C
4. A	9. B
5. D	10. C

Exercise 2

11. D	16. D
12. A	17. B
13. C	18. D
14. C	19. C
15. A	20. C

Lesson 11 Outer Space
Pages 41–42

Exercise 1

1. B	9. B
2. A	10. A
3. D	11. A
4. C	12. D
5. A	13. C
6. C	14. D
7. A	15. A
8. D	

Exercise 2

16. B A *meteorite* can be made of *metal;* a *shoe* can be made of *leather.*

17. D *Diffuse* is a synonym of *spread; close* is a synonym of *shut.*

18. A A *galaxy* is made up of *stars;* a *book* is made up of *pages.*

19. D *Elliptical* describes an elongated *circle; rectangular* describes an elongated *square.*

20. D *Extraterrestrial* is an antonym of *earthly; new* is an antonym of *old.*

Lesson 12 Science
Pages 43–44

Exercise 1

1. D	9. B
2. A	10. C
3. C	11. D
4. C	12. C
5. A	13. A
6. C	14. B
7. D	15. B
8. A	

Exercise 2

16. D A *geologist* is a person and *geology* is a subject; a *teacher* is a person and *history* is a subject.

17. A *Painstaking* is a synonym for *careful; small* is a synonym for *tiny.*

18. B A *biologist* uses a *microscope;* a *carpenter* uses a *hammer.*

19. A *Conserve* is an antonym for *waste; help* is an antonym for *hurt.*

20. D *Microscopic* describes the size of a *cell; huge* describes the size of a *mountain.*

Lesson 13 Earth Science
Pages 45–46

Exercise 1

1. C	6. D	11. B
2. A	7. A	12. A
3. D	8. B	13. C
4. C	9. C	14. B
5. B	10. D	15. D

Exercise 2

16. D A *fossil* can be an imprint in *rock;* a *footprint* can be an imprint in *mud.*
17. B *Bedrock* lies under the *soil;* a *floor* lies under a *rug.*
18. A A *glacier* is made of *ice;* a *sidewalk* is made of *concrete.*
19. C *Events* is a synonym for *phenomena; car* is a synonym for *auto.*
20. B A *prospector* hunts for *gold;* a *detective* hunts for *clues.*

Lesson 14 Aviation
Pages 47–48

Exercise 1

1. C	4. B	7. C	10. D
2. A	5. D	8. B	
3. D	6. C	9. C	

Exercise 2

11. C	14. D	17. A	20. C
12. A	15. A	18. B	
13. B	16. C	19. A	

Lesson 15 Health and Medicine
Pages 49–50

Exercise 1

1. B	4. A	7. B	10. C
2. A	5. C	8. C	
3. D	6. D	9. A	

Exercise 2

11. C	14. A	17. A	20. B
12. D	15. B	18. D	
13. C	16. D	19. C	

Lesson 16 Plants
Pages 51–52

Exercise 1

1. D	4. A	7. C	10. A
2. B	5. D	8. B	
3. C	6. B	9. C	

Exercise 2

11. A	14. C	17. C	20. A
12. D	15. B	18. A	
13. A	16. A	19. C	

Lesson 17 The Zoo
Pages 53–54

Exercise 1

1. B	6. A
2. A	7. C
3. D	8. B
4. C	9. D
5. D	10. A

Exercise 2

11. C	16. D
12. D	17. A
13. A	18. B
14. A	19. D
15. B	20. A

Lesson 18 Weather
Pages 55–56

Exercise 1

1. B	4. B	7. D	10. D
2. D	5. A	8. B	
3. C	6. C	9. A	

Exercise 2

11. C	14. C	17. C	20. A
12. D	15. B	18. A	
13. A	16. D	19. B	

Lesson 19 The Sea
Pages 57–58

Exercise 1

1. B	6. D
2. A	7. A
3. D	8. B
4. B	9. B
5. C	10. D

Exercise 2

11. B	14. D	17. A	20. A
12. C	15. C	18. C	
13. A	16. B	19. D	

Lesson 20 Travel
Pages 59–60

Exercise 1

1. C	6. D
2. D	7. A
3. A	8. C
4. B	9. A
5. C	10. D

Exercise 2

11. A	16. A
12. C	17. C
13. B	18. C
14. D	19. B
15. B	20. B

Lesson 21 Time and Measurement
Pages 61–62

Exercise 1

1. C	5. B	9. B	13. C
2. B	6. D	10. D	14. D
3. A	7. D	11. C	15. B
4. B	8. C	12. A	

Exercise 2

16. A A *diagram* is a type of *picture*; a *jar* is a type of *container*.
17. C *Expand* is an antonym of *contract*; *full* is an antonym of *empty*.
18. D A *protractor* measures the number of *degrees*; a *scale* measures the number of *ounces*.
19. A An *abacus* was a forerunner of the *calculator*; a *broom* was a forerunner of a *vacuum*.
20. B A *fathom* is a measure of *water*; an *acre* is a measure of *land*.

Lesson 22 Verbal Communication
Pages 63–64

Exercise 1

1. A	4. C	7. B	10. C
2. A	5. D	8. C	
3. D	6. A	9. D	

Exercise 2

11. C	16. C
12. B	17. B
13. D	18. A
14. A	19. D
15. D	20. B

Lesson 23 History
Pages 65–66

Exercise 1

1. C	6. A	11. A
2. B	7. C	12. D
3. A	8. B	13. B
4. B	9. D	14. C
5. D	10. C	15. A

Exercise 2

16. B *Enemy* is an antonym of *ally*; *loser* is an antonym of *winner*.
17. D *Brandish* is a way of displaying a *sword*; *wave* is a way of displaying a *flag*.
18. C *Copy* is a synonym of *emulate*; *assist* is a synonym of *help*.
19. D A *catapult* uses a *stone* for ammunition; a *gun* uses a *bullet* for ammunition.
20. A A *geneaology* is a history of a *family*; a *biography* is a history of a *person*.

Lesson 24 Government
Pages 67–68

Exercise 1

1. B	6. A
2. C	7. D
3. D	8. B
4. B	9. A
5. D	10. C

Exercise 2

11. C	16. B
12. B	17. D
13. D	18. B
14. C	19. C
15. A	20. A

Lesson 25 Agriculture
Pages 69–70

Exercise 1

1. C	6. D
2. D	7. C
3. A	8. A
4. B	9. B
5. B	10. A

Exercise 2

11. B	16. A
12. C	17. B
13. A	18. D
14. B	19. C
15. D	20. A

Lesson 26 Law
Pages 71–72

Exercise 1

1. A	6. B
2. C	7. C
3. C	8. D
4. D	9. A
5. A	10. C

Exercise 2

11. D	14. D	17. A	20. B
12. A	15. A	18. C	
13. C	16. C	19. D	

Lesson 27 Arts and Crafts
Pages 73–74

Exercise 1

1. C	4. D	7. A	10. A
2. A	5. B	8. B	
3. D	6. C	9. C	

Exercise 2

11. B	14. B	17. A	20. C
12. C	15. D	18. D	
13. A	16. C	19. C	

Lesson 28 Art and Music
Pages 75–76

Exercise 1

1. A	4. B	7. A	10. C
2. C	5. A	8. C	
3. D	6. C	9. A	

Exercise 2

11. D	14. B	17. A	20. B
12. C	15. A	18. B	
13. D	16. C	19. D	

Lesson 29 Construction
Pages 77–78

Exercise 1

1. B	4. D	7. B	10. B
2. D	5. B	8. A	
3. A	6. C	9. D	

Exercise 2

11. C	14. A	17. C	20. D
12. A	15. C	18. B	
13. D	16. D	19. A	

Lesson 30 Money and Finance
Pages 79–80

Exercise 1

1. A	5. C	9. D	13. C
2. B	6. A	10. C	14. A
3. D	7. C	11. A	15. D
4. B	8. B	12. B	

Exercise 2

16. D *Interest* is a payment for the use of *money; rent* is a payment for the use of *land.*
17. C *Affluent* is a synonym of *rich; happy* is a synonym of *merry.*
18. B A *depository* is a safe place for *valuables;* a *playpen* is a safe place for a *baby.*
19. A A *customer* needs service from a *clerk;* a *patient* needs service from a *doctor.*
20. A *Nominal* is an antonym of *large; quiet* is an antonym of *noisy.*

Lesson 31 Prefixes—*in-/im-/ir-*
Pages 81–82

Exercise 1

1. A	6. A
2. C	7. D
3. B	8. B
4. C	9. C
5. D	10. D

Exercise 2

11. A	14. C	17. A	20. B
12. C	15. C	18. B	
13. B	16. D	19. A	

Lesson 32 Prefixes—*after-/ante-/post-/pre-*
Pages 83–84

Exercise 1

1. B	6. D	11. D
2. D	7. C	12. B
3. C	8. B	13. C
4. B	9. D	14. C
5. A	10. A	15. B

Exercise 2

16. C *Posthaste* is a synonym of *swiftly; damp* is a synonym of *moist.*
17. B A *prelude* comes before an *opera;* a *foreword* comes before a *novel.*
18. A An *anteroom* is where you *wait;* a *bedroom* is where you *sleep.*
19. D *Posterity* are generations that come after; *forefathers* are generations that came before; *heirs* are relatives that come after; *ancestors* are relatives that came before.
20. A *Prevent* is the verb, *prevention* is the noun; *weigh* is the verb, *weight* is the noun.

Lesson 33 Clothing
Pages 85–86

Exercise 1

1. C	6. C
2. A	7. B
3. C	8. D
4. B	9. D
5. A	10. C

Exercise 2

11. C	16. A
12. C	17. C
13. D	18. B
14. A	19. A
15. B	20. D

Lesson 34 Nature
Pages 87–88

Exercise 1

1. D	6. A
2. C	7. B
3. B	8. C
4. B	9. B
5. D	10. A

Exercise 2

11. B	16. A
12. D	17. C
13. C	18. B
14. B	19. C
15. D	20. B

Lesson 35 Suffixes—
-ate/-en/-fy/-ize
Pages 89–90
Exercise 1

1. D	6. A	11. D
2. C	7. C	12. C
3. A	8. B	13. A
4. B	9. D	14. B
5. A	10. A	15. D

Exercise 2

16. B *Frighten* is a synonym of *scare; far* is a synonym of *distant.*
17. A *Activate* is a synonym of *stop; old* is a synonym of *young.*
18. D You *computerize* a process with a *computer;* you *automate* a process with a *machine.*
19. C You *fortify* using *weapons;* you *build* using *tools.*
20. B To *simplify* makes things *easier;* to *lock* makes things *safer.*

Lesson 36 Suffixes—
-ance/-ence/-dom/-ity
Pages 91–92
Exercise 1

1. B	6. B
2. A	7. C
3. D	8. D
4. A	9. D
5. C	10. A

Exercise 2

11. A	16. A
12. C	17. C
13. B	18. B
14. B	19. D
15. D	20. A